THE BIRMINGHAM
HOSPITALS CENTRE

A REPRODUCTION OF THE ETCHING OF THE HOSPITAL AND MEDICAL SCHOOL BY STANLEY ANDERSON, R.A.

Reproduced by courtesy of Sir Harry Vincent

THE BIRMINGHAM HOSPITALS CENTRE

by

STANLEY BARNES

M.D., D.Sc., F.R.C.P., (Hon.) LL.D., Birm.

CHAIRMAN OF THE EXECUTIVE BOARD
OF THE HOSPITALS CENTRE

*Formerly Physician to the General Hospital and
Physician (Neurologist) to the Queen Elizabeth
Hospital ; Dean of the Faculty of Medicine,
University of Birmingham, 1931 to 1941*

With a Foreword by

SYDNEY VERNON, LL.M.

PRO-CHANCELLOR OF THE UNIVERSITY
OF BIRMINGHAM

1952

Printed and Published by
STANFORD & MANN LTD.
BIRMINGHAM

THIS BOOK IS DEDICATED

to

THE MANY THOUSANDS OF MEN AND WOMEN

who by their

GOODWILL, INDUSTRY AND GENEROSITY

made possible the

BUILDING OF THE FIRST SECTION

of

THE BIRMINGHAM HOSPITALS CENTRE

namely

THE QUEEN ELIZABETH HOSPITAL

and

THE MEDICAL SCHOOL AT EDGBASTON

FOREWORD

IF the full story of all the Birmingham Voluntary Hospitals were to be written, it would be a wonderful record of wise foresight, bold adventure, intelligent planning and unceasing and unselfish service and generosity on the part of all classes of the community.

Until comparatively recently, all the Birmingham hospitals both general and special, were "Voluntary"; the latter group included the Eye, Ear and Throat, Skin, Women's, Maternity, and Dental. At the time of their foundation, both the General and Queen's were considered to be the last word in design.

The time came when, notwithstanding the provision of the Municipal hospitals, it was clear to certain far-sighted and public-spirited individuals that there was need, firstly, for a large and modern general hospital as a centre, secondly that it should be a teaching hospital, and accordingly that a commodious and well-equipped medical school should be in close proximity, and thirdly that this hospital should be so sited that special hospitals might be grouped around the Centre.

Dr. Barnes tells in this book an unvarnished tale of the origin of the scheme, of the troubles met with and overcome, and of the formation of the "Hospitals Centre" as a limited company to form an entity for organising the finance, controlling the expenditure and supervising the building. He also tells of the completion so far as was practicable of the great modern hospital now called the "Queen Elizabeth"; of the Nuffield Nurses' Home; and of the Medical School, which latter is a source of pride in the University of Birmingham, and the envy of professors of medicine and surgery in this and other countries.

Few men would have been so bold as to undertake the burden of such a gigantic project; fewer still would have had the ability, the tenacity and the determination requisite to organise this venture and to bring it to a successful conclusion.

The names of many generous donors and helpers are recorded; but three men stand pre-eminent in ability, devotion and unwearying effort; for without them the project could not have been brought to fruition. They are the late Sir Charles Grant Robertson (then the Vice-Chancellor of the University); Sir Harry Vincent, LL.D.; and Dr. Stanley Barnes, the author of this book.

Dr. Barnes, as Dean of the Medical Faculty of the University from June, 1931, to September, 1941, had the satisfaction of assuring himself officially of the perfection of the accomplished project.

As the Chairman of the Birmingham Hospitals Council, I formed a Committee to deal with the re-organisation of the general hospitals when the opening of the new hospital became imminent. Dr. Barnes tells in his book of the consequent closing of the Queen's as a general hospital; but one is happy to record that instead of ceasing to exist as a hospital, it was metamorphosed and became the Accident Hospital and Rehabilitation Centre which is doing magnificent work in its own specialised sphere.

One cannot read this book without a feeling of regret that the Nationalisation of the Health Service has put the stamp of officialdom on our hospitals and hospital services. Throughout the country, the provision of voluntary hospitals gave magnificent opportunities for unstinted co-operative enterprise and effort on the part of all classes of the community, and promoted a spirit of co-operation and independence. What may be the ultimate result of State control remains to be seen.

The readers of this book will, I am sure, join with me in congratulations to Dr. Barnes upon his excellent record of the Birmingham Hospitals, and particularly the story of the Hospitals Centre.

On his retirement from the Deanship of the Faculty of Medicine the University conferred upon him its highest honour, namely the Honorary Degree of Doctor of Laws. The Public Orator concluded his address in the following words:

"At last the Scheme became Reality. The edifice stood complete. The final touch of beauty was the Dean's Room, presented to the University by Stanley Barnes. Artistically, it is perfect in all respects, except that it is no longer adorned with his own genial presence. He has gone into another glorious trinity, that of the master-builders, whose monument we have only to look around us and see. Their names are Charles Grant Robertson, Harry Vincent and Stanley Barnes. The first two, when they rolled up their plans were enrolled among the Doctors of Laws. The third, as he rolls up his plans, receives the like honour. Inadequate though it be, it is yet the highest which the University can confer on the most devoted of her sons".

The name of Stanley Barnes will for ever be connected with the Medical School and the Hospitals Centre; not particularly because of his great financial generosity to the cause, but because he knew what he wanted, stood by his guns, produced it, and then quietly retired from the scene, some think without receiving full public acknowledgment of what to him was both a civic duty and a great source of pleasure.

SYDNEY VERNON.

vi

CONTENTS

LIST OF ILLUSTRATIONS

On the Cover. The Coat-of-Arms of the Queen Elizabeth Hospital.

Frontispiece. A reproduction of the etching of the Hospital and Medical School by Stanley Anderson, R.A.

TERMINOLOGY

A few definitions may help those readers of this book who are not conversant with the terms used in our hospital work, before the passing of the Health Act of 1946.

A VOLUNTARY HOSPITAL was one administered by an independent committee; it was supported by voluntary contributions from individuals and various organisations, but usually had no subsidy from rates or taxes.

A MUNICIPAL HOSPITAL was administered by the town or city, and was entirely supported through the rating authority.

A GENERAL HOSPITAL was usually voluntary in management. It would accept all types of patient, except cases of insanity, infectious disease, etc., Patients suffering from chronic diseases, and for whom no treatment was likely to be effective in saving life, were only rarely accepted, and then for short periods only.

A SPECIAL HOSPITAL was one which admitted as patients only those suffering from particular types of disease. Thus the Eye, the Ear and Throat, and the Dental Hospitals, all voluntary, were reserved for patients in whom corresponding disease was present.

A SPECIAL DEPARTMENT was one reserved in a General Hospital for cases similar to the above. Some General Hospitals reserved wards for a whole series of special departments, as did nearly all of those to which a Medical School was attached.

An ACUTE HOSPITAL is one designed to deal only with acutely ill patients, and whose stay in hospital is likely to be relatively short. Most of the general hospitals were of this type.

ANCILLARY is a term used to denote service of a medical character, but whose staff have no direct responsibility for the treatment of patients; for instance, X-rays, bacteriology and clinical pathology.

AUXILIARY refers to those other services necessary to any occupied building, such as heating, water supply, lighting, and kitchens and laundry.

AMENITIES are those items which cause a sense of pleasure, such as quietude, cheerful surroundings, and service with a smile.

In Birmingham, the term INFIRMARY usually denoted a type of hospital in which were housed chronic cases, such as those disabled permanently by accident, senility or disease. The Scottish use of this word corresponds to our hospital.

BIBLIOGRAPHY

The Roman Camps at Metchley, by Joseph and Shotton; Birm. Arch. Trans., Vol. LVIII, 1934.

Birmingham and its Regional Setting, by Kinvig, Smith and Wise; published by the Local Executive Committee for the British Association, 1950.

The City of Birmingham Handbook, City of Birmingham Information Department, 1950.

Domesday Book, for the County of Warwick, translated by W. Reader, of Warwick; 1087.

A School History of Warwickshire, by Bertram C. A. Windle; Methuen & Co., London, 1906.

Early Britain, by Jacquetta Hawkes; William Collins, London, 1945.

The Antiquities of Warwickshire, by Sir William Dugdale, 1656.

An History of Birmingham, by W. Hutton, 1795.

Birmingham, its Rise and Progress, by T. Lloyd Renshaw; published by Cornish Bros., Birmingham, 1932.

Bygone Warwickshire, by William Andrews; The Hull Press, Hull, 1893.

Sixty Centuries of Health and Physic, by Stubbs and Bligh; published by Sampson Low, Marston & Co., 1931.

Mediaeval Hospitals of England, by R. M. Clay; Methuen & Co., N.D.

Leland's Itinerary in England 1535 *to* 1543; Edition by Lucy Toulmein Smith, 1908.

The Birmingham School of Medicine, by Windle and Hillhouse; published by Hall and English, Birmingham, 1890.

William Sands Cox and the Birmingham Medical School, by J. T. J. Morrison; published by Cornish Bros., Birmingham, 1926.

The History of the Birmingham School of Medicine, by K. D. Wilkinson and others; published by Cornish Bros., Birmingham, 1925.

Our Birmingham, published by Cadbury Bros. Ltd., Birmingham, 1943.

The London Hospital Survey, by Gray and Topping; published by H.M. Stationery Office, 1945.

The Domesday Book of the Hospital Services, by Nuffield Trust, printed by the University Press, Oxford.

The Design and Construction of Industrial Buildings, by Moritz Kahn; London Technical Journals, 1917.

The Medical School of the University of Birmingham, by Stanley Barnes and others; published by The Medical School, 1939.

PREFACE AND ACKNOWLEDGMENTS

MY professional life has been closely bound up with the Hospitals and Medical School of Birmingham. As a student, as a Clinical Lecturer, and as Dean of the Faculty of Medicine, I have had an intimate view of our needs in medical education. As a member of the Staff of the Queen's Hospital, where I was successively House-Physician and Visiting Pathologist; and of the General Hospital as Assistant and later Honorary Physician; and as a Consulting Physician to several of the Special Hospitals in Birmingham and a few in the nearby towns, I had acquired a wide knowledge of the hospital services of the Midland Area.

I became a member of the Executive Board of the Hospitals Centre at its inception in 1927, and have remained a member ever since. I am now the Chairman of the Board, and it has been suggested to me that as I have a more complete knowledge than most of my colleagues of the story of its activities, and of the factors leading up to the building of the Queen Elizabeth Hospital and the New Medical School; and as the Board's activities are now much more circumscribed owing to the passing of the Health Act of 1946, I should put on record the history of the Centre Scheme.

For the opinions expressed, I alone am responsible. I expect that many of my colleagues, lay and medical, who were serving on the Boards and Committees of the various Voluntary Hospitals in this city, hold similar views about the effect of the Health Act, but it must not be assumed that either they or the members of the Executive Board of the Centre, necessarily agree with me.

In compiling this record, I have included, for the benefit of those readers who have little knowledge of the history of Birmingham and who wish to understand the basis on which we were transforming our hospitals system, a few pages on the history of our city as they affected our work. As we were ultimately to build on the site of a Roman Camp dating back to the first century, A.D., I have added a few notes to indicate the line of the Ryknield Street as it passed through Birmingham. Of necessity, these notes can only be brief, but if they whet the appetite of those who are archaeologically inclined, the various books to which reference is made in the bibliography will prove interesting.

The sorting out of the masses of records, minutes and press-cuttings which form the basis on which this book has been written, has been a tedious process, and I am greatly indebted for that work to my friend Mr. J. C. N. Burrow, M.A. (OXON); the minutes consulted include many of the Board and Committees of the General Hospital, similar records from the Queen's Hospital and the Hospitals' Council, and of course from the Executive Board of the Hospitals Centre and its committees. The press-cutting records of the two hospitals and the Medical School have also been perused and relevant letters and leaders abstracted. Mr. Burrow has also been good enough to sort out and aggregate the list of Subscribers to the Appeal, a laborious task for which I am profoundly grateful to him.

Of the many friends who have helped me in the preparation of this book, I must mention in particular Sir Harry Vincent. The successful issue of the Centre Scheme was very largely due to his energy, his drive, and his generosity; he has kindly allowed me to reproduce herewith the etching prepared for him by Mr. Stanley Anderson, which shews the School and the Hospital when viewed from the base of the University Tower. Mr. Eric Vincent, who is recording in so many beautiful publications the contemporary history of the University, has also been of very great assistance, and has kindly allowed me to make use of some of his illustrations.

Apart from many professional colleagues, I am indebted to the Secretary of the University, Mr. C. G. Burton; and the Assistant Registrar of the University, Mr. Cyril Snead; to the House Governor of the Queen's and later of the Queen Elizabeth Hospitals, Mr. G. Hurford; to Mr. P. Crocker at the General Hospital; Mr. F. W. Bradnock, the Public Relations Officer of the city of Birmingham; and the distinguished architect of the new and very beautiful King Edward's School, so near to the Centre, Mr. Holland W. Hobbiss.

Above all, I am indebted to my old friend and colleague, Mr. Sydney Vernon. He has been intimately associated with the Hospitals Centre since the early days, has been a member of the Board of Management of the General Hospital, and was Chairman of the Hospitals Council from 1937 to 1947; the University of Birmingham is to be congratulated upon his acceptance of the Office of Pro-Chancellor, in which capacity he is the business head of the University. Throughout our somewhat tempestuous period of planning and building, he was in close touch with most of the principal supporters and many of those others who took the other view. From start to finish, he was a consistent advocate of the Centre, and gave of his best in allaying opposition and helping the Scheme forward. He has added to my debt to him by reading proofs, and by writing an all too appreciative foreword.

There is a large group of our citizens and friends to whom the Executive Board will wish me, as their present Chairman, to offer our thanks. Throughout the twenty-four years since we were constituted, and mainly during the fourteen years of our planning and building activity, we received no less than £1,189,968, of which sum about one-tenth was allocated to the University for the building of the Medical School. I still marvel that in days when money was so much more valuable than it is today, we were able to induce our friends to make such a magnificent voluntary contribution to our hospital work. To one and all of the generous donors, on behalf of the Hospitals Centre I offer our cordial thanks, and I am sure that they have the gratitude of the whole of the Midland area served by the Queen Elizabeth Hospital. Without their unstinted generosity, our work would have been impossible. It is a matter for regret that in the supplement giving the list of our subscribers, it has been impossible to include the names of donors of sums smaller than £10. It is not that we did not appreciate these smaller sums, for we knew that they often came from homes where a few pence a week may have meant the sacrifice of some greatly-prized luxury. Usually these smaller sums were included in the collective contributions, and we, the Appeals and Building Committees, never knew the names of the actual donors. The contributors of these smaller sums were throughout our most consistent supporters; they were a tower of strength during the controversy, when the whole scheme appeared to be in jeopardy.

Edgbaston, 1952.   STANLEY BARNES.

INTRODUCTION

THE practice of medicine has changed very rapidly in the last hundred years. Apart from other changes, there has been a progressive tendency not only for individual members of the profession, but for institutions to be segregated for the purpose of treating special types of disease. In consequence, a whole series of Special Hospitals has been founded, usually independent of any General Hospital, and each managed by an entirely independent committee. All these hospitals were of the Voluntary type, and as the public and the Press both greatly favoured continued specialisation, the establishment of more and more Special types of hospital was to be expected.

There is no doubt that the tempo of research has been increased by such concentration by Specialists, and that the benefits of their work have been made available more widely than would otherwise have been possible. There are, however, certain drawbacks to the system of Special Hospitals, discussed more particularly on pages 55 and 56, which are only imperfectly understood by those who have no technical knowledge, and which those of us who were acting as officers to such hospitals were most anxious to remove.

The need for a widespread increase in the number of beds in Birmingham in the 'twenties' of this century, combined with the necessity for rebuilding the Medical School near the newer section of the University at Edgbaston, provided an opportunity for a possible re-organisation.

The fundamental basis on which the Hospitals Centre Scheme was founded, was the building of a constellation of hospitals all near the Medical School, and all within a stone's throw of one another. In this way, we hoped to improve the treatment of our patients—always kept in mind as the first consideration—and at the same time to provide for a better system of medical education and an increased opportunity of research. (See diagram on page 89).

The first hospital building in such a scheme was to be the general one, partly because we in Birmingham needed general beds more urgently than special ones, and partly that it would need to be available for medical education, and closely associated with the Medical School geographically as well as administratively. It was intended that as and when opportunity offered, the Special Hospitals in the City of Birmingham would move from the centre of the city to the site. It is to be noted that all of the hospitals concerned were Voluntary ones, and that all made provision only for acute cases.

So far as management of the various hospitals was concerned, we intended to leave each hospital to be independent; there was no question of their being absorbed by or made subject to, the general hospital. We had in mind that when a special hospital came to build on the site, there would be an agreed policy on such matters as the architectural form and the facing bricks to be used. It would thus be possible to avoid loss of dignity in design, which had so often disfigured our city in the past, when buildings of clashing styles had been set up side by side. It was also hoped that a common system of heating, and several other auxiliary services might be shared with the general hospital and the Medical School, to mutual financial advantage. Yet another way in which expense might be avoided if the other Voluntary Hospitals could be re-built on adjacent sites, was in the reduction of personnel needed for the service of the ancillary departments; for, given sympathetic management of the University and the various hospitals grouped around the School, there would be a great saving in the staffs necessary.

We had hoped that in the not too distant future, it would have been possible to set up also an Institute of Nursing on the site, and that similar economies in nursing staff, and particularly in the number of those engaged in teaching nurses, would be possible here whilst greatly improving the education, both academic and practical, of the nurses attached to all the hospitals on the site.

It is true that to many of our friends, the main function of the Hospitals Centre was to make good a deficiency in the number of beds available for patients in Birmingham. To those of us who were associated with the actual building, the deficiency merely constituted the occasion on which a start might be made on a comprehensive scheme of re-construction.

It will be noted that the Medical School was to be the focus around which the constellation of hospitals was to be built. At the moment of our planning in 1925, the Medical School, which constituted the Faculty of Medicine in the University, was located in the centre of the city, occupying a part of the Mason College building in Great Charles Street. For several years, the University of Birmingham had been in process of re-building its faculties at Edgbaston, and already the Faculty of Science was housed there. The University Council was anxious at the earliest opportunity to move the Faculty of Medicine to a site adjacent to the Science departments, for many students needed to receive instruction from departments in both faculties. It seemed, therefore, that this was a favourable opportunity to combine the re-development of our hospital service, with a re-building of the Medical School, providing that suitable land could be made available.

It was obvious that such a comprehensive scheme of development could only be effectively brought about over a long period of time. What was needed in the first place was a sufficient area of land, in the right place and carefully reserved for the future buildings which would be necessary. Looking back over the history of the older voluntary hospitals, we had come to realise that they had built for their immediate needs, and that when the time came to expand and provide a larger or more modern type of service, there was no nearby land available.

It will be realised that to inaugurate such a comprehensive scheme, there would be required the consent if not the co-operation of a large number of independent councils, boards and committees. It will also be seen that such a development in the city would need the support of the City Council, who, through their Health Committee which managed the Municipal Hospitals, were likely to be affected by such a widespread change.

We, the Executive Board of the Hospitals Centre, have often been criticised for being so slow in getting off the mark in our building. Had we been in a dictatorial position, and able and willing to ride rough-shod over the opinions of those who directed the other charities in the city, we should certainly have got on more quickly, but is was essential that we should carry public opinion with us if we were to collect from voluntary subscriptions the very large sum that would be necessary in the first place.

For the inauguration of the scheme, and after the munificent gift of the land next to the University at Edgbaston by Messrs. Cadbury, we decided to build the Medical School and the most urgently needed of the hospitals, the one for acute general cases. This general hospital, now called the Queen Elizabeth, and the Medical School were so far complete as to be ready for occupation only a few months before the Second World War broke out.

Even before the Queen Elizabeth Hospital was in occupation, preliminary steps had been taken for the re-building on the Centre Site of some of the Special Hospitals. Not only had very considerable sums of money been collected, but sketch plans had been prepared and sizes determined for the Dental, the Maternity and the Ear and Throat Hospitals. The Centre Board had prepared a plan for the layout of the site; it involved the cutting of a new road from Follows' Farm to the lower part of the westerly approach road near the *Golden Cross*, and it was around this new road that the hospitals were to be grouped. The allocations still required the assent of the City Council, who are the owners of the Centre Site. In the same way, the provision made for a Nursing Institute on the site still needed the approval of the City Council.

No action to re-build the Special Hospitals, rapidly becoming as starved of elbow-room as were the General and the Queen's in the twenties of this century, could be undertaken until the two other buildings were ready for occupation in 1939. During the next few months, the international situation was so clouded by the threat of war, that only preliminary work was possible. The war and its aftermath, followed by the Health Act of 1946, have made redundant any further work by the Executive Board of the Centre, or the committees of the Special Hospitals. Only the Ministry of Health can now determine what further building, if any, may be erected on the Centre Site.

As is known to all, the State is short of money—and seems likely to continue to be short of money—with which to finance additional building. If one looks back to the years 1930 and 1931, when the general financial condition was still more serious than it is today, both the Government and the Municipal experts advised against our carrying on, despite the fact that our work would help to remedy the widespread unemployment of those days. The delays resulting from those official pronouncements caused a start of actual building to be held up till January of 1933, and the loss to the hospital can best be realised when we find that the increase in the cost of materials, etc., meant that we had to pay as much for the 540-bed hospital as would have covered the cost of the 750-bed hospital that had been designed in the first instance.

It was largely local patriotism that enabled us to appeal so successfully for funds. Many of us, perhaps wedded to the Voluntary system because we had seen the magnificent work it had accomplished over the centuries, regret that such appeals as we then made are no longer in the range of practical politics. To-day, no decision as to re-building the other hospitals on the Centre Site, can be made locally; any recommendation so to act must receive the assent of a body which has no special concern for Birmingham, and whose interests are directed to a levelling process, which generally means mediocrity, rather than to the establishment of a high level of hospital development that might become a target for every other region in the country.

When the building was so far complete that it was possible to hand it over for management to the United Hospital, the President of that body paid a glowing tribute to the work of the Hospitals Centre, when thanking them for their enterprise and devotion, which had produced so excellent a result after fifteen years of voluntary effort.

After the hospital, now called the Queen Elizabeth, had been erected, a clause insisted upon by the Board of Trade in our Memorandum, prevented our handing over the buildings to the United Hospital, and the Hospitals Centre remained the technical owners. I understand, from notes that have appeared in the Press, that our cherished possession, the Queen Elizabeth Hospital, on which we lavished so many years of hard work, and to which our citizens gave so much of their savings, has been "expropriated" by the Ministry of Health. We should have regarded it as an act of courtesy if the Minister of Health or one of his responsible officials had informed us directly of the decision, and the blow would have been softened if a word of thanks had been added in appreciation of the work so diligently carried out by the Hospitals Centre.

The future of the Hospitals Centre Site appears at the moment (1952) to be in doubt. What is fairly certain is that the Hospitals Centre Executive Board, including the Building Committee responsible for the building of the Queen Elizabeth Hospital as the first section of the Centre Scheme, is not likely to be consulted in any further use of the site. Already some of the land, so generously given by Messrs. Cadbury, and reserved for the purpose of hospital development in the deed of gift to the City, has been used for the erection of some 200 houses. To many of us, it seems hopelessly wrong that the city, the actual owners of the site, should have permitted such a breach of trust. They cannot hope for many years to come that other generous gifts of the same type will be made, when the donors fear, as now they must, that the object of their benefactions may be diverted into other channels for reasons of expediency.

If the powers that be should decide to build other hospitals on the site, it is hoped that every effort will be made by those who have the well-being of our City at heart, to ensure that the same form of building and the same type of facing brick are used in the new construction. The form of building adopted for the Queen Elizabeth Hospital and the Medical School involves a minimum of waste, for there is no unused room in either building. They are also so constructed that the maximum use can be made of machines for cleaning and maintenance. Any attempt to imitate the styles of the older hospitals must involve a higher rate of expense as well as detracting from the architectural amenity of the group of buildings on the Centre Site.

For good or ill, the Voluntary Hospital system has gone. It is for us to make the best of the new State system that has taken its place. I hope that those, both lay and medical, who have succeeded us in the management and staffing of our hospitals, will do their utmost to see that the high standard that was set up by the Voluntary Hospitals is not allowed to lapse. I have no doubt that some of the smaller hospitals may well be brought up to a higher standard of efficiency than was possible for them under voluntary control, but I cannot yet see any sign of progress in those great institutions where a Medical School is attached to a Hospital, and which set the pace for our whole system of healing. Let us hope that the spirit of the Voluntary Hospitals will not be crushed by the lifeless hand of bureaucracy, and that in time, as it becomes obvious even to the public that the Voluntary system gave us a better and more progressive order of healing, there will come about some form of devolution which will once more make it possible to arouse local patriotism.

CHAPTER I

BIRMINGHAM THROUGH THE AGES

THE opinion generally held by archaeologists is that the area now occupied by Birmingham and the adjacent Black Country, was largely covered by forest in the years before the Roman invasion of A.D. 43. At what can only be a rough estimate, the population of Britain in those days would be about a million, and most of the tribes would live either in the coastal areas, along the course of the main rivers, or in forest clearings. In the Midland region, the forest of Arden extended from the Cotswolds to Cannock Chase, but there were many clearings, particularly in the higher ground. The lower reaches, traversed by such rivers as the Tame, the Rea, and the Avon, were very marshy, owing to the river beds being so often blocked by fallen trees and other vegetable débris, and in consequence any travellers kept to the higher land wherever possible. It is presumed that a forest track preceded the building by the Romans of the road which was to be of interest to us two thousand years later.

The decision of the Emperor Claudius to colonise Britain led to the building of military roads, and of these two of the first were the Fosse-way and the Watling Street. The former, starting from Axmouth in Devonshire pursued a course in a north-easterly direction to York; whilst the Watling Street starting from Canterbury, passed through London, and gradually bending more westerly as it traversed the centre of England, reached Chester; its line is today largely that of the Holyhead Road and the North-western Railway line to Holyhead.

These two were arterial roads, as we should now call them, but as time went on several secondary roads were constructed. Of these, the Ryknield Street, from Southampton to Tynemouth, was one of the most important. Thwarting the Fosse at Bourton-on-the-Water, it followed a course almost due north to reach the Watling Street at Wall. As in all cases where a military road was made, rest-camps or "marching camps" were constructed at intervals of a Roman Day's journey—about twenty Roman miles or sixteen of our modern English miles.

The first marching camp on the Ryknield Street after leaving Bourton northwards, was at Alcester, or as the Romans called the nearby camp, Alauna. The next camp, sixteen miles further north, was at Metchley, whose Roman name has not come down to us; it was on the site of this camp that we were to build the new Medical School and the Queen Elizabeth Hospital in the thirties of this century. After leaving Metchley, the Street traversed what is now the city of Birmingham, and the name is preserved in the "Icknield Street", which follows fairly closely the

1

line of the old Ryknield Street. After crossing the river Tame at Hockley, the Street ran northwards through Streetly to reach the Watling Street at Wall, or Etocetum as the Romans called the nearby fortified station.

The researches carried out during our building operations by Joseph and Shotton indicated that Metchley was not a fortified camp, permanently occupied by a Roman garrison, but was only constructed for the protection of the army on the march; indeed, the suggestion derived from the débris found, is that the first army to remain camped there, of about half-legionary strength, only remained for a few days. Some years later, another Roman army passed this way, and the original camp being too large for this army to defend, a second series of earthworks was thrown up inside the first camp; it is suggested from the size of this smaller camp that the strength of the army on the second occasion was about two cohorts, but again there was no permanent occupation of the camp.

Just as it is likely that the Romans used a forest track that had been made by their predecessors the ancient Britons, so their successors, the civilian population of the district, would use this highway for their trade. We have no written record of what happened to the Ryknield Street or to the area on which Birmingham now stands, after the Romans left in 410, until the compilation of Domesday Book in 1087. As Birmingham is there mentioned by name, it is to be assumed that it had already been in existence for some years, and many speculations are put forward for the origin of the name. One that has found favour with some archaeologists, is put forward by Renshaw, and is to the effect that when Ceawlin, the Saxon ruler who flourished from 560 to 593, advanced westwards and northwards with his victorious army, taking by storm the cities of Bath, Gloucester and Cirencester, and destroying the Roman city of Uriconium, he established the advanced base of his conquests at Wednesbury (Woden's burgh), and took steps to guard his line of communications. For this purpose, he had to choose trustworthy men, and one of the tribes so used had the generic name of "Brem". They would be called "Bremings" in their day, and this name forms the clue to the names of several towns in the midland area. Thus, the group detached for duty south of the Lickey Hills formed a grove—"graf" in Saxon times—and founded Bromsgrove. Another group, just north of the Lickeys, formed a "hame" or home, which became known as the "Breminghame"; others were to give their name to such settlements as West Bromwich, Castle Bromwich, etc. Whatever the origin of the name Birmingham, its spelling over the centuries since Domesday has appeared in written documents in no less than a hundred and forty different ways.

It is probable that the foundation of Birmingham as a small hamlet took place about two hundred years after the Romans left in A.D. 410. When the Domesday record was compiled, in the years 1080 to 1087, it was mentioned that "Bremingha'" had been "held freely by Ulwine" in the reign of Edward the Confessor (circa 1050). Of Birmingham, the record runs that "Richard holds of William four Hides", the William being presumably the Earl FitzAnculf who came over with the Conqueror,

2

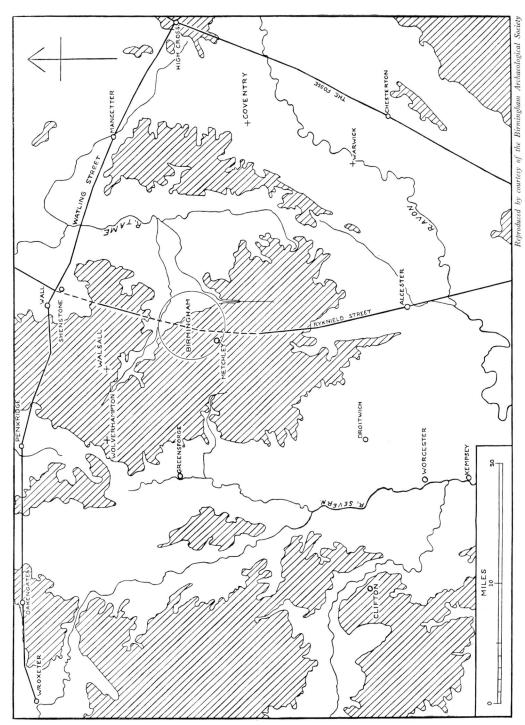

MAP OF THE SEVERN AND AVON VALLEYS   O = *Roman sites mentioned in the text*   + = *Sites of other towns*

The land above 400 feet is shaded

Reproduced by courtesy of the Birmingham Archaeological Society

and Richard, also presumably a Norman, the founder of the De Bermingham family. The other places of interest to us that were mentioned in Domesday were Edgbaston (Celboldestone), smaller in extent but of equal importance to the King's valuers, Aston, Northfield, Handsworth and Harborne, now all more or less absorbed in the City of Birmingham.

Birmingham itself was then only a small village, near the Manor House of the De Berminghams. It lay on the main route from Coventry to Lichfield, just where the road crossed the river Rea, and after the two still smaller hamlets, Deritend and Digbeth had been passed. There is no record of the number of the inhabitants, but it must have been very small, and probably did not reach one hundred.

Metchley is within the parish of Edgbaston, and it was only when the site was examined by Joseph and Shotton in 1934 that fairly conclusive evidence was obtained that this had been a Roman Camp. Hutton, an earlier historian of the Midlands, wrote in 1783: "In Metchley Park, three miles west of Birmingham, in the parish of Edgbaston, is the Camp; which might be ascribed to the Romans, lying within two or three stones cast of the Ikenield Street, where it divides the counties of Warwick and Worcester, but is too extensive for that people. . . . it must therefore, have been the work of those pilfering vermin the Danes, better acquainted with other peoples' property than their own. . . .".

At a later date, John Finch, another local historian, published a plan giving the measurements of the site and of the two camps, in 1822. He came to the conclusion that this was a Roman Camp, and that it was a half-way house between the camps at Alauna and Etocetum, each being a Roman day's journey distant.

The researches of Joseph and Shotton have confirmed the deductions of Finch, and those who are interested in archaeology will find many of the odd bits of Samian ware unearthed during our excavations, preserved in a case in the Medical School, where also maps, prepared under the direction of the authors mentioned above, indicate the position of the camp and the location of the findings.

One of the first steps which led to the development of Birmingham as we know it today, was the right granted in 1166 by the King to Peter de Bermingham to hold a market once a week. This concession, a greatly important one in those days, especially to an agricultural community, was never revoked, and it made the village of Birmingham the market centre of the whole district for five or six miles in all directions.

In the later years of the thirteenth century, there was established the Priory, and this is the earliest written record that has come down to us of a "hospital" in Birmingham. The hospitals of that period appear to have been of three classes; some were leper houses, and at this period in English history it is estimated that there were some two to three hundred such hospitals in the kingdom. A second group accommodated wayfarers, more especially pilgrims and merchants, and it was this type of hospital which gave the name to the group. The third type were what we today would call alms-houses, and in them were accommodated the poor and destitute, and perhaps a small number of sick. There was of course nothing comparable to the hospitals of today; these early hospitals were all administered by ecclesiastical authorities.

Of the Priory, nothing now remains in Birmingham but the name. In 1382, there was founded the Gild of the Holy Cross, which was destined to be an important factor in the life of Birmingham. Although in the first instance a purely religious organisation, it soon took over certain civic functions, such as the education of children, the maintenance of roads and bridges, etc. The Gild shared the fate of so many religious institutions, was suppressed and the endowments seized by Henry the Eighth; but at the request of the citizens, a considerable part of the endowments was returned by Edward the Sixth, and applied to the founding of the Grammar Schools which bear his name to this day.

As to the exact period when metal working became a common occupation in this area, there is much doubt. Hutton (1795), in his "History of Birmingham", puts forward the conjecture that the Britons who fought against the Romans were armed with "sword, spear, shield and scythe" and that these weapons were not imported but were supplied "with those necessary implements by the black artists of the Birmingham forge" (Page 23). What is certain is that when John Leland visited Birmingham in one of his Itineraries, metal working on a large scale was being practised here. His description of the town in 1540 is as follows:

"I cam thoroughe a praty strete or evar I enteryd into Bremischam toune. This strete, as I remember, is caullyd Dyrtey, in it dwells smithes and cuttelers, and there is a brooke that debydithe this strete from Bremischa. Dyrtey is but an hamlet or membre longynge to (Aston) paroche therby and is clene separated from Bremischam paroche.

"There is at the end of Dyrtey a propre chaple and mansion howse of tymbar, hard on the rype as the brooke cummithe downe, and as I went thrwghe the fords by the bridge, the water ran downe on the ryght hond, and a fewe miles lowere goithe into Tame rypa dextra.

"This broke risethe, as some say, a 4 or 5 miles above Bremicham toward the Blake hills in Worcestershire. This broke above Dyrtey brekethe into 2 armes that a litle benethe the bridge close agayne.

"The bewty of Bremischam, a good market towne in the extreme partes that way of Warwiks-shire, is in one strete goynge up alonge almoste from the lefte ripe of the broke up a mene hille by the lengthe of a quarter of a mile. I saw but one paroche churche in the towne. There be many smithes in the towne that use to make knives and all maner of cuttynge tooles, and many lorimars that make byts, and a greate many naylors. So that a great parte of the towne is mayntayned by smithes.

"The smithes there have yren out of Staffordshire and Warwikeshire and see coale out of Staffordshire".

Dugdale in 1656, commences his chapter on "Bermingham" thus: "This being a place very eminent for most commodities made of iron . . . . But that its appelation was originally taken from some antient owner thereof, or planter in the Saxons time, need not be doubted, the last part of it, viz. ham, denoting a home or dwelling and the former manifesting itself to be a proper name". Dugdale makes no further reference to the industries of the region, as he was chiefly interested in the genealogy of the nobility and gentry, and matters ecclesiastical. Nevertheless, the illustration on the same page (655) shewing the prospect of Birmingham from Ravenhurst near the London Road, on the south-east part of the town, clearly indicates that even at this date the town was sparsely populated, the houses being clustered around Digbeth and the Bull Ring.

It will be noted that the town was still largely an agricultural community; today, in 1952, no one approaching from King's Norton along Deritend ("Dyrtey"), would describe this as a pretty street. It will be noted also that Deritend was outside the boundary of the town, and was in fact in the parish of Aston; both of these townships have now been absorbed into the city of Birmingham. Note also that the spelling of the name of the town had not yet been fixed in its present form, and that Leland uses two and Dugdale another of the hundred and forty-one ways of spelling that have been used in documents and printed works since the Norman Conquest. It is also noteworthy that coal from Staffordshire was even in Leland's day replacing the charcoal from the oaks of Arden as the source of heat for smelting the iron.

In the civil war of the seventeenth century, Birmingham was one of the main sources of supply of arms for the Parliamentary army, and this was one of the reasons why Prince Rupert in 1643, on his way from Worcester to Chester, spent a night at Camp Hill, then near but now included in the city, and the following day sent his troops to pillage and fire the town. From those days onwards, there is abundant evidence that Birmingham was one of the main centres in the country for the making of munitions, though similar work for civil purposes was always available for our citizens in peacetime.

The eighteenth century was one of major importance to Birmingham. A factory had been set up at Soho by Boulton, where for the first time water-power was supplemented by steam-power. After being joined by Watt, the firm supplied some of the earliest steam-engines for mines, particularly in Cornwall. This was one of the first of the big factories to be established in England, and by 1774 was employing over a thousand people in "the fabrication of buttons, boxes, buckles, trinkets, etc., in gold and silver.... Their excellent ornamental pieces have been greatly admired by the Nobility and Gentry, not only of this Kingdom but all Europe...." (Swinney).

It was during this period that there flourished in Birmingham and the district the Lunar Society, which included in its members Boulton; John Baskerville, the printer; Samuel Galton; Lloyd, the forerunner of the banking and insurance family; Erasmus Darwin, the grandfather of the still better known Charles; Josiah Wedgwood, the potter; Joseph Priestley, the discoverer of oxygen; James Watt, the engineer; and William Withering, the physician to the General Hospital at its opening in 1779, who introduced digitalis to the medical profession as a remedy for dropsy. Meetings

6

occurred regularly and this group of men, with a few members who lived nearby, constituted much of the intellectual driving force which was to cause so rapid an expansion of the trade of Birmingham and of its population during the next century.

The progress of Birmingham during the eighteenth and nineteenth centuries coincides largely with the "industrial era"; it also covers much of the period in which the General and Queen's Hospitals were founded and flourished, and to which reference has been made when describing these two institutions. Here it must suffice to say that the development of the town—now a city—progressed rapidly as power was applied to industry, and that the drift from the country to the towns continued with ever increasing speed. Whenever this country went to war, or was preparing to meet aggression from elsewhere, more and more agriculturists changed their occupations and came into the factories. Of the many who thus came to Birmingham, very few left after the emergency was over; they stayed to swell the ranks of the artisans, for they found the amenities of town life more to their liking than the relative solitude of the country.

As always, here and elsewhere, the housing of these newcomers lagged behind what was desirable. Every effort was made by the municipal authorities to cope with the influx, and as the opportunity offered, slums that had developed were swept away and houses built elsewhere. Much still remains to be done to get rid of the out-of-date back-to-back houses near the centre of the city, and to provide the household amenities that have become almost necessities today.

Birmingham has one great advantage which is a result of the foresight of the city fathers of the nineties of last century. The scheme by which water was collected some eighty miles away in the Elan and Claerwen valleys in Wales, and transmitted through a series of conduits to Frankley Reservoir, and thereafter served to the city at the rate of some thirty to fifty million gallons a day, has been an outstanding success; it gives to the householder and the industrialist an unfailing supply of pure soft water. Although the initial cost of the dams and aqueducts was large, and for years the water rates had to be subsidised, there is no doubt that this scheme has been an inestimable boon to our city; for the river on which Birmingham stands, the Rea, would not suffice for one tenth of the number of inhabitants, even when supplemented by the numerous artesian wells which have been sunk in the Kueper Sandstone. The city owes much to Sir Thomas Martineau and his committee of 1892, for providing what is one of the best—if not the best—water supplies of any city in the British Isles. Only the existence of this water supply has made possible the development of Birmingham as we see it today.

It is not necessary here to give a detailed account of the Birmingham of 1920 to 1930, when we were called upon to initiate the Centre Scheme. It will have been gathered from the previous notes that this was a thriving community, chiefly engaged in manufacture, and particularly of metal ware of all kinds; the city had grown very rapidly from the time when the industrial revolution had begun, and over-crowding in the centre with transformation in the earlier days of dwelling houses into workshops, had left a very considerable leeway to be made up in the housing of the people. The continued presence of these slums meant that we were bound to face a higher disease rate and to require more hospital accommodation than might be expected where such defects in housing had not developed; but they affected but little the work of an acute hospital such as the one we were contemplating in 1927.

Two factors of rapidly increasing importance had developed during the previous twenty years. The increase in power-driven machines in industry had involved an accident rate that could not have been expected in earlier years, when the "New" General Hospital was designed for instance, in 1892. The substitution of motor cars for horse-drawn traffic was another cause of increase in the number of accidents for which the hospitals were expected to allow, and the provision for them, in a city where expansion was going on so rapidly, urgently demanded special attention. Add that during the first world war, as during the second, a large proportion of those who remained at home were engaged in munition work, and that little new building had been possible, and it will be readily understood that it was the misfortune of our civic leaders rather than their fault, that the provision for our hospital work had become so insufficient.

Census figures for the City of Birmingham were available for the use of our Hospitals Centre Committee when we formed our estimates of what would be necessary in our hospital work in the year 1927. The provision that we contemplated was not confined to the inhabitants of the city alone, but covered a considerable area of the adjacent "Black Country". As we were intending to build on the Voluntary Hospital principle, we needed therefore to make an allowance for those living outside the city boundaries; and experience over several recent years gave us an average of some thirty per cent. higher than the provision which would have had to be made for the city alone. It may, therefore, be of interest to set out the census figures, and in order to complete the picture, I give such earlier and later figures as are available up to 1951. They are as follows:

1087 (Domesday)	? 100		1801	.. .. ..	73,670
1546 (Leland) ..	2,300		1821	.. .. ..	107,000
1650	5,472		1851	.. .. ..	233,000
1700 (Westley) ..	15,000		1881	.. .. ..	401,000
1731	23,000		1901	.. .. ..	522,000
			1921	.. .. ..	922,000
			1931	.. .. ..	1,002,000
			1951	.. .. ..	1,110,000

Much of the very large increase in population over the last hundred years has resulted from the inclusion in the city of many adjacent townships, which have thus become suburbs of Birmingham.

It would have simplified our task in determining how many acute beds were necessary in 1927, and would be required by 1931, when we were hopeful that the

Centre Hospital would be available, and by 1951, a date for which we were also trying to make provision, if the Hospital figures available had been divided into categories. In the overall figures presented to us in our preliminary meetings in 1926-7 were included many beds for chronic patients, and for these we were not making any provision. In recent years, since the Queen Elizabeth Hospital was opened, such figures have become available to some extent, not only for our city but for the country at large. So far as our hospital population was concerned, it was generally agreed that beds were insufficient in 1926, but four years later, when the controversy arose, and before a brick had been laid on the Metchley site, the rather poorly-digested mass of figures given to us by various authorities when compared with those of 1926, gave rise to much doubt in the minds of those responsible for making the provision necessary, as to whether any new hospital was in fact needed. (See also, pages 48-49).

CHAPTER II

THE BACKGROUND.
SOCIAL AND MEDICAL PROGRESS

IT is only possible to understand the causes that underlay the policy which determined the building of the Hospitals Centre in Birmingham, if the reader has some
knowledge of the prevailing social conditions, of the progress of medicine and
surgery up to the period of the nineteen-twenties, and of the possibilities that some
of us saw were likely to be available.

In the early days of this century, it was regarded as a reproach to their social
status if a member of the middle class became either an out-patient or an in-patient
at a voluntary hospital; if he needed in-patient treatment or an operation, it would
be done either at his own home or at a nursing home. Even before the war broke
out in 1914, the social barrier was crumbling, partly because the hospitals were
now getting better results, and partly because of the increased cost of operations.

By the end of the war in 1918, the distinction between the middle and artisan
classes had, so far as the hospitals were concerned, largely disappeared, and only a
few of the larger nursing homes were able to give such good service as the hospitals.
It still remained true that the discipline in the latter, and the absence of amenities
like wall decorations and flowers, gave the nursing home advantages, and the privacy
so deeply cherished by some patients was often an overwhelming argument in
their favour.

The war in 1914 to 1918, was a great leveller so far as social differences were
concerned. Many of the middle-class men who served in the ranks, had become
accustomed to close association with men whom their fathers would have considered
it demeaning to accept as friends; they had often been treated in hospitals with
men of the artisan class as their companions, and on their return to "blighty", they
were no longer concerned to be segregated in a nursing home. The fact that taxes
now made prohibitive to many such a luxury when free treatment could be obtained
at a voluntary hospital, was often the determining reason why so many of a class
that before had never thought of going into a hospital, now preferred admission
there to any other home where adequate treatment might be available.

This widening of the social classes demanding treatment at the hospitals was
not the only cause of the intense pressure put upon them in 1920. The population
of Birmingham and the surrounding district which the voluntary hospitals so largely
served, had increased by leaps and bounds. The demand for munition workers,

10

many of them from the countryside, had reinforced the natural increase in the area, and the difficulty of making adequate provision for them was seen both in the over-crowding of the houses and the troubles of the hospitals. True, that the Municipal Hospitals were doing their best to make up the hospital deficiences, and that, as the Army vacated the Dudley Road building, the city had continued to use this hospital, as had the Army before them, as an acute hospital, instead of accommo-dating here only chronic patients.

For one reason or another, most of the patients preferred to come to the voluntary hospitals. This was no fault of the municipality, but occurred largely because the General and Queen's, with a hundred years of reputation behind them, were well known to the public, while the Municipal Hospitals had still to establish their reputation with the citizens at large. Medicine is a very personal subject; it often happens that a prospective patient consults friends and especially medical friends, as to whom he shall visit with the idea of an operation or of treatment by a physician in a hospital. The system by which the voluntary hospitals had staffed their hospitals, rendered easy the fraternisation of the consultant who was the honorary officer at the hospital with the general practitioner. The latter would get to know exactly what type of patient he should send to particular physicians and surgeons. No such close co-operation was possible in the setting up of whole-time officers by the Municipal Hospitals; it would take a much longer time for their reputation to become known to the general practitioners, and then it would often be only indirectly through such patients as had been treated. Again, the honorary officers at the voluntary hospitals had often been the tutors of the practitioner, and their knowledge of one another's capacities and idiosyncrasies was being maintained by their frequent meetings at consultations and medical societies.

The pressure on the voluntary hospitals due to social changes and the rapid increase in population, were not the only reasons why we wished to build afresh. Although we wanted more beds, we wanted many other things as well.

PROGRESS IN MEDICAL TREATMENT—

SURGERY

Those who have only become aware of the conditions in our hospitals during the last thirty years may like to be reminded of the history of hospital treatment generally during the previous century, when most of the hospitals were built. At the beginning of the nineteenth century, there were no anaesthetics, and a surgical operation of any major character was a fearsome ordeal which could only be faced by a patient in an emergency, and was only performed by a few bold spirits of the type of Abernethy.

The introduction of anaesthetics in the middle of the century inaugurated a new era. Surgery was now no longer such a repellent practice that only the superman would face it. Nevertheless, there was no vast increase in the numbers of operations

11

performed, for the death rate from post-operative sepsis remained very high, and in addition, there was always the risk of some epidemic spreading through the hospital wards from patient to patient. Operations which involved the opening of the peritoneum were barred, as the risk of death from peritonitis was something approaching a hundred per cent.

The next big advance in surgery came as a result of the new knowledge of bacteria. In the latter part of the century, Lister, applying to surgery the work of Pasteur in biology, began to use the carbolic spray to prevent the infection of wounds made by the surgeon.

Quickly the use of antiseptics in this way was abandoned when it was found that the even better results, without the corresponding dangers, could be attained by asepsis; instead of killing the germs in the atmosphere and on the instruments, steps were now taken to see that they never reached the patient's wound. Needless to say, the technique of aseptic surgery was only established gradually, but by the turn of the century all the most progressive surgeons were operating in sterilised white gowns instead of discarded frock coats, and before another ten years had passed, practically all surgeons wore rubber gloves, to prevent possible infection from their own hands; and insisted that all those who entered an operating theatre should wear masks to prevent any septic particles from floating about in the atmosphere.

As a result of these changes in the technique of operations, the death-rate dropped enormously. Similar arrangements were made in the wards, the sister and dressers using face-masks and freshly sterilised gloves for each patient; the spread of infection from one patient to another now became so rare a phenomenon, that a special enquiry would often be set up to determine how such an unexpected accident had occurred. It was at this period that began the Golden Age for Surgery. The number of operations went up by leaps and bounds. A hospital like the "New General", built in the nineties and designed in the year 1890, had represented the latest ideas in theatre accommodation. Whereas the "Old General" in Summer Lane could with difficulty cope with six hundred operations a year, the new hospital was designed to deal with a thousand. In actual fact, within twenty years of the opening of the new hospital in 1897, the number had risen to nearly fifteen thousand, and all sorts of adaptations had to be made, sometimes at the expense of sorely needed hospital beds, to make this work possible.

Even so, the adaptations were only imperfectly successful. There was no convenient place where the surgeon and his assistants could properly carry out those ablutions, and don the gloves, wellingtons, gowns and masks, so necessary for all who were in the theatre. Still less was there any place where the students who were acting as dressers could don their theatre overalls. It was ironical that just as we had solved this problem, yet another cropped up in the provision that had to be made for women medical students. Although Mrs. Grundy was dead, or at least moribund, neither the hospital authorities nor the parents of the students liked

12

the idea of the two sexes using the same dressing room, for, as most surgeons demanded a theatre temperature approaching eighty degrees Fahrenheit, robing for an operation meant for all a certain amount of disrobing also. For a time this trouble was met by getting the Theatre Sister to allow the women students to use her room, so carefully guarded from sepsis, but the sister was never happy with this makeshift arrangement.

The first twenty-five years of this century were the golden years of surgery. It is not to be supposed that no further advances have been made since then, but they have been rather in the direction of developing such special surgery as that of the head or chest, and there is no evidence of a widespread increase in the numbers demanding surgical operative treatment during the succeeding quarter century. The demands on surgical hospital accommodation have therefore advanced less rapidly, and, unless some new discovery should be forthcoming, we may assume that the space required in a hospital for surgery will correspond roughly to increases in the population, and will not require any of those major changes which were necessary twenty-five years ago.

MEDICINE

Medicine, as distinct from surgery, had made no spectacular progress up to the turn of the century. From the days of Hippocrates in Cos in the fifth century B.C., there had been relatively little progress in our knowledge of disease till the nineteenth century, when diagnosis—the fundamental science of medicine—began to assume great importance. During last century, most of the diseases to which flesh is heir were sorted out and put in their correct pigeon-holes; there remained a few of the rarer ones, and doubtless there will be some new ones, which will also need to be investigated and segregated, but unless some new method of investigation arises, the work of diagnosis had been largely completed. As an example we may remember the confusion that formerly existed between the two fevers, enteric and typhus, one spread by infected milk and the other by insect bites, and which was only cleared up finally when the bacteriologist was able to demonstrate the two different organisms concerned. Towards the end of last century, men of light and leading in the medical profession were becoming increasingly impressed with the value of bacteriological investigation, but the knowledge was not yet common to all those senior officers who were teaching clinical medicine, and were often assisting to direct the policy and construction of our hospitals.

Bio-chemistry first came to the aid of our diagnosis less than fifty years ago, and has been of increasing importance year by year; clinical pathology is another ancillary service with which no modern physician would care to dispense, whilst the knowledge obtained from the pathological department is of fundamental importance.

A discovery in physics which was to mean more than any other ancillary service to medicine occurred in 1896, when Roentgen published his work on X-rays. The gradual application of this new discovery added very greatly to the diagnosis of disease, and not a little to its treatment; but it took over twenty years for those who were responsible for the building of our hospitals, to realise how important a new weapon had been added to the arsenal of the physician and surgeon, and how much space and staff were necessary if the best use were to be made of the rays.

No voluntary hospital in Birmingham had been built (I speak of the year 1925) since X-rays had become essential for the proper working of an acute hospital. Since they were built, all existing hospitals had been compelled to set up an X-ray department in such space as was available and often without adequate regard to the convenience of its location. The result had been that in most hospitals the managing committees found it necessary at frequent intervals to issue to the staffs requests or demands that the number of films exposed for X-ray work should be reduced, and not only the expense but the pressure on the department as a whole should be diminished. Similar requests are still issuing in the year 1952, but the medical staffs, it may be with an ear turned to the possible caustic observations of a coroner, usually reduce their demands on the X-ray department only for a few days, and then revert to what they regard as normal practice.

There is another reason why these adaptations often fall short of the ideal; high-tension electric currents are used, and the rays have great penetrating power; this is particularly true of the rays used for treatment. The safety of both patients and staff must be assured in any ideal installation, or indeed in any such department which operates on a large scale.

I have suggested above that the first quarter of this century was the Golden Age of Surgery. When, in 1927, we were designing the Queen Elizabeth Hospital, many of us believed that a similar advance in Medicine was just round the corner. We therefore designed our new hospital to take full advantage of the new knowledge, and while still continuing to make the welfare of our patients our primary object, to forward medical education and research. Our expectations have been more than fulfilled, and it may well be said by the historian of the future, that the second quarter of the twentieth century was the Golden Age of Medicine. The earlier treatment that was euphemistically called "expectant", which meant trusting to nature and the normal reactions of the body to disease to meet the trouble, has given place to forms of treatment in which anti-biotics, made in the laboratory instead of the human body, can be applied so rapidly as to cut short many diseases. Most people have heard of M.& B., and of the wonderful effects of Penicillin, but there is a whole host of other new drugs now available, each developed to deal with its own type of bacterial disease. Insulin, an animal extract produced in the laboratory, and a large group of other hormones are now made to substitute some vital secretion which, for some reason or other, may have ceased to be provided naturally. Although the end is not yet in sight, in the last twenty-five years there has been more progress in the *treatment* of disease than in the previous millenium.

There is not and probably never will be, any panacea which can be used to combat one and all of the diseases from which man suffers. A drug which is excellent for typhoid is practically useless for typhus, and septic pneumonia cannot be treated on the same lines as that due to the pneumococcus. It is not therefore possible, nor is it within the range of probability, to dispense with the clinical laboratory or the bacteriologist. The more precise the diagnosis, the more likely it is that the most suitable drug will be used. Most of the bacterial diseases are now under control, and those due to flagellate organisms may soon cease to be a menace to mankind. It is true that some of the diseases, chiefly of virus origin like influenza and the common cold, have not yet been subjugated, but the appearance in the last few years of the electron microscope, which now for the first time gives a picture of the viruses, has provided a new weapon in the armoury of the investigator, which may lead to the ultimate control or elimination of these and similar virus diseases.

To make the best use of the new knowledge, it was clear that at the end of the First World War, many more facilities must be put at the disposal of the medical staff than had been available when the hospitals had been built before the year 1900. Apart then from the increase in the number of beds which were necessary, it was important for any first-class acute hospital, to install within its walls all those special or ancillary services to which reference has been made. All must be available on the spot, and all—especially the X-ray department—should be sited in the right place.

I have made no mention here of the accommodation for out-patients and casualties. As we, in our new building never reached the stage of putting up those two departments, a few words only may suffice. The out-patient department of a general hospital should, wherever possible, be separated from the casualty, lest the in-coming cases of accident, often muddy and blood-stained, should need to be carried through a crowd of waiting out-patients. No arrangements of this sort had been made in the "New General" in 1897, and with the increase in the number of road accidents, and the increasing reliance of the factory group on hospital treatment, the number of casualties had so far increased as to swamp the out-patient department. By 1920, we at the General were dealing with 50,000 casualties a year, and although this included a considerable number of relatively minor injuries, yet the number requiring anaesthetics for operation had reached 5,000. The original Casualty Department was hopelessly insufficient, and must be re-constructed elsewhere.

CHAPTER III

THE GENERAL HOSPITAL

THE mediaeval hospital in England was rather "an ecclesiastical than a medical institution, for care rather than cure, for the relief of the body when possible, but pre-eminently for the refreshment of the soul" (R. M. Clay). Even at the beginning

THE FIRST GENERAL HOSPITAL, 1791

of the eighteenth century, the only public institutions for the reception and treatment of the sick poor were St. Bartholomews and St. Thomas's Hospitals, both in London. In the provinces, "private charity was the sole alternative to parish relief." (G. C. Peachy, quoted by Stubbs and Bligh, p. 220).

The eighteenth century was marked by the founding of many hospitals in London and the provinces. In Birmingham, the General Hospital was founded through the benevolence, energy and persistence of Dr. John Ash. Although the first steps were taken in 1765, it was 1779 before the hospital in Summer Lane "near the town of Birmingham" was opened for the reception of patients.

Birmingham then had a population of about 40,000, and the only other provision for the sick poor appears to have been the Town Infirmary, a poor-law institution with 270 in-patients and 752 out-patients. The surgeon to the Infirmary was Mr. John Tomlinson, and "actuated by a desire for instructing the young gentlemen of the Faculty educated here, a course of anatomical lectures was attempted during

16

the winter of 1767 to 1768". Tomlinson was one of the first surgeons appointed to the new General Hospital, and probably continued to teach medical students there. He was one of the first, if not *the* first, of the provincial surgeons to give a regular course of lectures to medical students, though occasional lectures had been given before that date, even in Birmingham.

The first General Hospital was built to house about 100 patients, and it is an interesting contrast to modern conditions to note that four nurses were appointed at a salary of four guineas per annum, with the promise of "an additional guinea if they behave well". The barber was paid 10/6 per quarter to shave the patients twice a week.

It is not necessary to trace here in detail the development of the General Hospital throughout the next hundred years. It need only be said that the hospital progressed, both in numbers of beds available and in the character of the treatment. The population of the town was increasing rapidly throughout the century, as manufacture, especially of metal ware, tended to concentrate near the coal fields. By the end of last century the population of the city had reached half a million, and as the Hospital had always accepted patients both from within and without the city boundaries, it was serving an even larger number.

By 1890, it became clear to some of those directing policy at the General Hospital, that to bring the hospital up to date, it would be better to rebuild on a new site than to try to alter the old building. The two great figures in the building of the new hospital in Steelhouse Lane were Sir John Holder and his friend, the young surgeon, Mr. Gilbert Barling, and it was their enthusiasm and hard work that resulted in the construction of the building in Steelhouse Lane.

When opened for the reception of patients in 1897, the "New General Hospital" represented the last word in hospital construction in Europe. Externally, its somewhat florid style with its many terra-cotta ornamentations was greatly admired, and although modern taste usually prefers a simpler façade, the general impression is one of dignity, and even may be considered imposing. The site was near the centre of the city, and was restricted in every direction; it occupied practically the whole of an island, bounded by Steelhouse Lane, Loveday Street, Weaman Row and Weaman Street. The main ward blocks were of three storeys each, all the wards having high ceilings to permit of an ample air space for all patients; basements under the wards and under the administrative block provided accommodation for stores; the heating and ventilation were by the Plenum system, whereby air, filtered, warmed and moistened was supplied to the wards and rooms throughout by a series of ducts. Between the ward blocks, sufficient spaces had been left to permit of the free circulation of air, to allow a maximum of light to reach the wards, and to permit of the making of lawns.

In planning the building, it was evident that the architect had in mind that this was the last word, and that no material expansion, or alteration in equipment necessitating increased accommodation would be required; indeed, any other than minor alterations would not only destroy its architectural attractions, but reduce its efficiency.

The "New General" was opened in 1897, and admirably served its purpose for several years. The plenum system of ventilation resulted in a great saving in laundry expense, and there was a general atmosphere of cleanliness that was rarely to be seen elsewhere without an army of scrubbers. On the other hand, most of the house-officers complained of headaches and malaise, and children seemed to wilt when deprived of the atmosphere to which they were accustomed.

These, however, were minor troubles. Our real difficulties began when any attempt to provide extra accommodation was needed, and when any variation in the internal structure was required, in order that we might adapt the hospital to rapidly changing demands, of surgery more particularly, but to some extent of medicine as well.

I have described elsewhere the progress which was being made in both branches of medicine, and they largely corresponded with the first twenty years of the life of the new hospital.

One of the first of the new types of officer to be appointed was the almoner, whose function it was to see that necessary help was given to in-patients after they had left hospital, and before they were fit once more for earning their living. She also needed on many occasions to help the out-patients, many of whose ailments were more due to malnutrition than to disease. Where was this new officer to be located? In those days, the main out-patient hall would often be filled by a thousand patients, waiting to see one or another of the physicians or surgeons, and it was a tight squeeze to find any place where she could be suitably housed.

By 1907, we needed a massage department, which was later to grow into the department of physio-therapy. This time, the only casualty ward was used for a time, in the hope that there would be no recurrence of the wholesale demands made upon these few beds as on former occasions. Within a year to two, the demands on the massage department had so far grown, that much wider space was required, and the carpenter's shop in the basement was annexed for the purpose. By this time an X-ray department was needed, and although for a time a section of the surgical out-patient accommodation had been transformed, it soon became evident that more, much more, space was needed; this time, other basement rooms, designed for stores were annexed.

The out-patient department had by now become grossly overloaded. Apart from the increase in numbers consonant with the increase in population, there had arisen since the hospital was designed a progressive specialisation. The out-patient department had been built to accommodate, apart from medicine and surgery, only one speciality, gynaecology. By 1920, we had, in some way, to accommodate a dental, an eye, an ear and throat, a skin department and one for venereal disease; and it was evident that others—like the asthma and diabetic clinics—were going to be

18

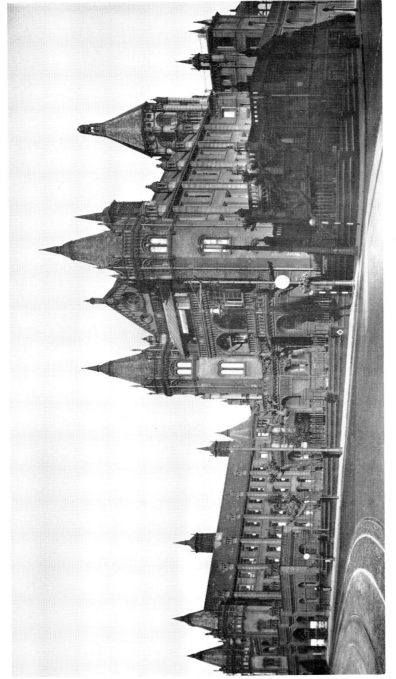

THE SECOND GENERAL HOSPITAL

19

necessary. Even if we got rid of the casualty department, it would be impossible to accommodate all these extra specialities without encroaching on the bed accommodation, which was in those days the last thing we should have done.

All the adaptations we made were insufficient to meet the growing demands of the city. The more we adopted new adjuvants to treatment, the more the sick population clamoured to be admitted as patients. By 1922, the number of acute hospital beds in Birmingham was represented by a figure about 2.7 per thousand, a hopelessly small figure for a city whose inhabitants were mainly earning their living by manufacture. The waiting lists of the surgeons grew to absurd dimensions, and a man with uncomplicated hernia stood little chance of admission within two years. On the medical side, the position was different, but only because a mere fraction of the urgent cases, such as pneumonia, were admitted, for it was useless to put them on a waiting list.

By the end of the war, in 1918, the position had become intolerable for the staff, who were responsible for the selection of those to be admitted. Naturally the war had accentuated the difficulties, but it soon became evident that even after the armistice, when the shooting war had ended, the pressure was not likely to be abated.

Elsewhere, I have sketched in brief outline the new knowledge which was now available, and many of our physicians and surgeons who had served abroad or at other hospitals, had learned the value of those ancillary services. The days had gone when a member of the staff could be expected to do Wassermann tests, to search a film for malarial organisms, or to do elaborate tests on the excretions to discover if any trace could be found of pathogenic bacteria, or of some chemical substance which indicated a particular type of disease. It was no answer to these questions to tell us to send specimens elsewhere; for often the organisms would die in the post owing to lowering of the temperature. Besides, the Board did their utmost to avoid such an expenditure as would be represented by the number of such examinations by outside agencies, and we, the staff, wanted the officers doing these tests to be at our own hospital and immediately available. If the demands of surgery were more obvious to the lay members of the Board, those of us who practised as physicians were certain that provision for our needs was no less urgent.

In 1920, I became chairman of the Medical Committee, and as such it would be my duty to represent to the Board of Management the opinions of the medical staff. As I listened to the various complaints and the difficulties that beset every department, it became obvious that what was needed was something far more than a mere re-shuffling of beds or re-allocation of existing space for other purposes. We needed more space, and the space was likely to be much more than could be found on the existing site.

We set up a series of sub-committees of the Medical Committee, to represent every subject in which we, the staff, were interested. It was wearisome work for men who were deeply interested in their profession, but after some nine months, the reports were at last presented to the full committee. After a general discussion,

I drew up a comprehensive report, which included such of the recommendations as the Medical Committee as a whole had approved.

Our report was presented to the Board in December, 1922. We asked for an addition of 130 beds for patients, a doubling of the accommodation and a trebling of the equipment of the X-ray department; four new (additional) operating theatres, with a special lift reserved for their use; more accommodation for casualties (accidents and emergencies), with the necessary observation wards, a fifty per cent. increase in the out-patient department, with recovery rooms for patients after out-patient operations; and special accommodation for venereal disease. The list concluded with a request for a wide increase in the space available for physio-therapy, and the provision of new departments for bio-chemistry and clinical pathology.

It will be noted that no mention is made of the extra nurses who would be necessary. This omission was in accordance with the traditions of the General Hospital, where any nursing suggestions always originated in the House Committee. Although this point had been in mind all the time, we were too anxious not to jeopardise the decision on the main questions for us to tread upon anyone else's toes.

It need hardly be said that the extent of these requests came as a great shock to the lay members of the Board of Management. After all, the hospital was only twenty-five years old, and already some £70,000 had been spent on alterations. Many of the members had been on the Board when, as the last word, the "New General" had been opened for use in 1897. I well remember my interview with Mr. Sidney Goodwin, the Chairman of the House Committee, the day before the formal presentation of the report. "Impossible. Do you know what this will cost? Over a hundred thousand pounds". I replied that I was afraid it would be nearer double that figure if we included equipment.

Needless to add, the Board only accepted the scheme after the most searching enquiry, but eventually it was decided that it was impossible to maintain the reputation of the hospital and to give, as we had done in the past, a first-class service to the city, unless steps were taken to carry into effect the recommendations of the medical committee.

For this purpose, there was set up a committee of the Board, known as the Extension Committee. It contained both lay and medical members, and was directed by the Board to advise how these changes could be made and what would be the cost of the alteration and additions.

THE EXTENSION COMMITTEE

This Committee was set up in January, 1923, and although I had ceased to be Chairman of the Medical Committee, I was asked to become a member as I had taken so prominent a part in reparing the report to the Board. The chairman was Mr. Douglas V. Johnstone, the chairman of the Board of Management, and the other members were Mr. Sidney Goodwin, chairman of the House Committee;

Mr. Leonard P. Gamgee, the senior surgeon; Miss H. Bartleet; the Rev. W. S. Houghton; Mr. J. C. Vaudrey; Mr. T. Ratcliff and Mr. J. E. Wilcox.

With the help of the architect, an examination was made of all the possibilities for extending on the existing site. At first, it was hoped that by putting an extra storey on each of the existing ward blocks, it might be possible to give us something like what we needed, but the form of construction of the original building and the character of the foundations made such an alteration impossible. As the original open spaces left between the ward blocks had already been largely filled in, there was no hope that anything like what was needed could be obtained on the original site.

At the back of the hospital was St. Mary's Church, with a graveyard attached which had been but rarely used since 1840. The church had been built in 1774, when it was in the centre of a thriving residential community, but over the years this section of Birmingham had been transformed into a series of small workshops, chiefly in the gun trade. So few parishioners now remained in residence there that the attendance at services in the church rarely reached double figures, though the seating accommodation was originally for some six hundred. The church was separated from the hospital by a little-used street, Weaman Row, and it was therefore decided to approach the ecclesiastical authorities with a view to buying the church site, and to obtain the authorisation necessary to close and absorb Weaman Row.

After negotiations lasting for many months, it was found necessary to promote a Private Bill in Parliament in order to carry through the purchase of the church site and to obtain permission to close the road. Eventually the Act of Parliament gave us permission, and the price paid to the church authorities was agreed at about £17,000; the church was to be demolished at our expense, and the graves cleared and the human remains re-interred at an agreed cemetery.

Needless to say, these negotiations and legal formalities took a long time to mature, and during this period sketch plans were prepared and rough estimates were made out as to the cost. We had obtained our Act of Parliament by 1925, and had reached a stage when the church was demolished, but we had not yet got possession of the land; that conveyance could only be made after we had cleared the cemetery, and this expense was estimated at something approaching £10,000, for the whole of the acre and a half had to be sieved to a depth of some nine feet. We were thus committed to an expenditure of something like £30,000, without having obtained a single one of our urgently needed additions.

The total estimated expenditure, including that on the church site, was £250,000. This amount would give us about 130 beds extra, and the cost of this item was put at £31,000, the rest being required for the site, out-patient and casualty departments, engineering, nurses' home and school, theatres, septic block, venereal department, and the new scientific departments, administration and alterations to frontage.

One of the conditions laid down by the Voluntary Hospitals' Commission in the making of a Government grant to the voluntary hospitals—our share at the General was £8,000—was that in any proposed extention involving the addition of beds or a public appeal for funds, we were to bring the case before the Local Voluntary Hospitals Committee. This Committee had by 1925 merged with the Joint Hospitals Council to form the Hospitals Council for the City of Birmingham, and whatever the legal position might be, we agreed that morally, the promise we had given to the first-named body, was still binding on us to bring the matter forward again, when, "after proceeding with their negotiations, the scheme was further advanced".

In accordance with this resolution, the General Hospital now brought forward a report of the position, and gave the estimate of the costs. The meeting of the Hospitals Council was held in October, 1925, some three years after the original resolution had been passed. At this meeting, which of course represented all types of hospitals, voluntary and municipal, and included nominees of the City Council, I was asked by my colleagues, as the one who knew most about the technical aspects of the case, to represent our case to the Council. While I was speaking, to my amazement one of our representatives to whom I had been speaking only a few hours before, and with whom I had had daily consultations for some weeks, interjected a remark which made it clear to everyone concerned that he no longer supported the scheme. Those who have read the notes on the relationships between the various hospitals will realise that thereafter, we should not have a ghost of a chance of receiving a unanimously affirmative vote; the result was that the Council approved the following resolution:

"That no decision be taken on the proposal to extend the bed accommodation of the General Hospital in the centre of the city until full enquiry has been made through the Ministry of Health and other available sources as to the comparative cost and efficiency of general hospital extension in open surburban areas as compared with the extension on central sites".

I have summed up in a few words the work done by our Extension Committee at the General Hospital; I need hardly say that to get so far had meant a very trying time for all of us and particularly for some of us who had spent nearly five years to reach this stage; for the medical men involved, we had sacrificed what should have been our hours devoted to private practice, to the writing or reading of papers on technical subjects so essential to our professional status, or to some form of recreation. Only our devotion to the hospital of which we were so proud would have made us use up so much of our time in committee work. Like myself, Gamgee was deeply interested in his profession; as a surgeon, and Professor of Surgery at the University, he was at the zenith of his career, and was regarded by all of us as the leading surgeon in the Midlands. I never heard the opinions of all the lay members of our Board on the result of the Council's resolution, but when at a single blow, all of our years of intensive work was shattered, one of them put it to me that it was the work of "an irresponsible body of men who had no interest in the General Hospital".

23

The resolution only called upon us to "halt", but those of us who had been working at the scheme knew without any peradventure that the scheme was dead. It is true that a few looked round to see if we could not regain the freedom we lost when we joined the Local Council and accepted the £8,000. Many suggested a subscription to repay this amount, and wash our hands of the Hospitals Council. Others, more suspicious, saw in this move an attempt so to depress the standard of the General that the Municipality could step in and say, "You are no longer competent" and take over control. Yet another suggestion was to buy still further land, and if, as was rumoured, the University rebuilt the Medical School at Edgbaston, and intended to use the nearby Selly Oak Municipal Hospital as the main clinical building, we should revivify the old Sydenham College, and so found a second medical school in Birmingham. I never came across any member of our staff in those days of bitter disappointment who believed that our scheme had been turned down on its merits.

It was only slowly that tempers cooled, but the position of the staff was becoming intolerable. The pressure on the beds was intense and the provision of ancillary services was far behind what was known to be available at the rival Municipal Hospitals. What was almost equally galling, was that the Queen's, who had not had the two years' wait needed to get an Act of Parliament, were now so far advanced in their building that they could look with complacency on the dictum of the Hospitals Council; for a building that is up to the first storey must be finished, or it will become an object of derision to those who stop its completion.

It is worth while at this stage, to indicate what happened to the arrested Extension Scheme of the General Hospital. Although it had been intended by the Hospitals Council that the arrest should be complete, the long delay in making alternative accommodation available at Edgbaston determined the General Hospital to make at least fairly adequate provision for Casualties. In fact, a series of "temporary" buildings was erected on the St. Mary's site, and when they were opened by Sir Gilbert Barling in November, 1930, he said that it was expected to treat up to 40,000 casualties in each year; actually, the number reached 52,000 within a couple of years. The opening of this Casualty block provided a very valuable relief to the out-patient department, and it is still working at a high level of occupancy despite the subsequent foundation of the Accident Hospital in Bath Row. The cost of the buildings was about £45,000.

CHAPTER IV

THE QUEEN'S HOSPITAL

THE Queen's Hospital was built primarily for the purpose of clinical instruction to Queen's College medical students.   Up to 1840, the General Hospital had been used for this purpose, but the increasing numbers of the students made it desirable

THE QUEEN'S HOSPITAL, 1841

to look round for further opportunities for clinical instruction.   No doubt other reasons reinforced this desire to have a hospital built; the town was rapidly extending, and the population was increasing by leaps and bounds, so that further hospital provision was overdue.   In addition, it might well be argued that as the dean of the medical school (Sands Cox) was not on the staff of the General, the position of students in the school over which he presided, was less secure at the General Hospital than it should be, or might become if a new hospital were available.   In his letter to J. T. Law in November, 1839, which was intended to be published as a pamphlet appealing for support for the building of the new hospital, Sands Cox brought forward many points in support.   He concluded: "The institution would aim, not at rivalry with any other, but believing that the sphere that demands

25

the interposition of human benevolence in behalf of an innumerable multitude of our unfortunate fellow-creatures, suffering under the calamities of disease and accident, is yet too large to be adequately provided for by existing establishments; it would claim to enlist itself in the honourable service; and whilst its primary object must be to afford relief to the sick and maimed poor, it would become the storehouse of authenticated medical facts; would extend the boundaries of medical science; would advance the welfare and happiness of mankind; would give the parent the means of educating his son for a physician or surgeon beneath his own eye; and in connection with the Grammar School, by drawing to the town families for the purpose of professional education, it would indirectly promote our prosperity; while we should thus be prepared to see eventually realised the prophetic and expanded views of our venerated and esteemed President, expressed at the anniversary dinner, June 4th, 1831, that 'Birmingham will become the seat of a Central University'.

This letter, written in 1839, gives an idea of the breadth and scope of Sands Cox's ambitions for the school that he was setting up. The urge to expand into a University grew upon him as time progressed, and it was because he had not the patience to wait till such departments as he had established were self-supporting before he set up new ones, that the whole edifice to which he devoted his life came near to complete collapse.

The Queen's Hospital was opened with about a hundred beds in 1841; in 1845, the detached block for infectious cases was opened with 28 beds; in 1850, two wards were added, and the dispensary and operating rooms enlarged; in 1868, the adjoining house and grounds of St. Martin's Rectory were acquired, and five years later the new out-patients department was opened. This period is also noteworthy for the setting up of the Hospital Saturday Fund, largely at the instance of Mr. Sampson Gamgee, who was surgeon to the Queen's Hospital at this time.

The Nurses' Home was erected in 1887, the operating theatre modernised in 1893, the Nurses' Home was extended again in 1908, and a series of new wards, chiefly for medical cases was opened at the same time. By now, the bed accommodation for patients numbered 178, and for nurses, 74. At the same time, the opportunity was taken to modernise much of the surgical accommodation and equipment, and to extend the engineering and heating services.

The Extension Scheme which was arrested by the fiat of the Hospitals Council in 1925, included the erection of wards to house a hundred additional patients, and at the time of the Council's resolution, the new buildings had reached the first storey stage; it was obviously necessary to complete these ward blocks, but all the other ancillary services that had been planned were left incomplete. No wonder the Chairman, at the Annual Meeting of the Governors in 1927, said that it looked as though the Queen's Hospital "had been condemned to a lingering death".

It will have been noted that the Queen's Hospital was built at the instance of the Dean of the Medical School, which was already in existence in Paradise Street. Most of those who gave large sums of money to enable the buildings in Bath Row to be erected were either clergymen, like Warneford, or were strong supporters of the Anglican Church, like J. T. Law, the Chancellor of the Diocese of Lichfield. Sands Cox was the grandson of one clergyman and the nephew of another, and was throughout imbued with strong religious principles—to him religion meant the Church of England, and no other. The setting up of a Faculty of Theology at Queen's College was the natural step for such governors to undertake, and it thus came about that the Queen's Hospital in its early years was dominated by a strong clerical element; it was only after the passage of an Act of Parliament in 1867, that the Hospital was entirely freed from control by those who governed Queen's College. It was at this period that the latter body had become insolvent, owing to the establishment of a series of departments with expensive staffs in theology, engineering, law, mathematics, modern languages, Latin, Greek, and architecture. Sands Cox had moved too fast, and although the original department of medicine was still flourishing, there was no such surplus of funds from this faculty as would finance all the others that had been established.

By the Act of 1867, the Queen's Hospital was separated so far as all legal commitments were concerned from Queen's College, and from now onwards the staff were appointed by the Governors of the former body. There remained the close working agreement for the training of medical students, and in the new Act, it was still an obligation on the Hospital to receive for training in clinical work all the medical students of Queen's College.

It may be convenient here to jump forward some ten years, and to follow the fortunes of the building in Bath Row, known for a hundred years as the Queen's Hospital. In 1937, when the Queen Elizabeth Hospital was nearing completion, all the steps necessary to safeguard the position of the staffs of both the General and Queen's had been taken; this was true of the medical, nursing and administrative officers. I tried to work out in my own mind—I was Dean of the Faculty of Medicine at that time—what would be the position of the Queen's in a few years after the new hospital had come into being. For many reasons, I came to the conclusion that as a unit of the United Hospital, responsible for the clinical teaching of our students, it must lose ground when compared with the other two units. The Extension Scheme of the Queen's had been arrested in 1925 at the same time as the similar scheme for the General; but the wards for the accommodation of patients, already built up to the first floor, had been completed to house an extra 100 patients. The consequence was that the Hospital was overloaded with beds, and that there was a shortage of space for nurses, and also for those ancillary services so essential to a modern acute hospital designed for the teaching of medical students.

It will be remembered that Sir Charles Hyde, the proprietor of the *Birmingham Post* and the *Birmingham Mail*, the two most influential papers published in the Midlands, had been on the Queen's Committee for years, and had later become its President.

27

It seemed to me to be likely that if a scheme to eliminate from the United Hospital a building so dear to him were sprung upon him without notice, there would again arise an uproar in the Press corresponding to that of seven years before. I therefore asked Sir Charles for a personal interview, and in October, 1937, spent a morning and afternoon with him at Berkswell. I put before him all the facts as I knew them, and as I expected there was at first a very stormy response; but after lunch and a very good glass of port, and after he had realised that I did not propose that the Queen's building should be destroyed but only diverted to other hospital uses, and in a much calmer atmosphere, he asked why had I come to him. I explained that it was because I was not prepared to ask any colleagues once more to face a Press campaign like that of 1930-1931, and that unless he could assure me that there would be at least neutrality so far as his papers were concerned, I was not prepared to bring forward the scheme. I told him that what I had in mind was the use of the building for one of the "specialties", for which it could be suited at but little expense, as the number of ancillary services needed would be on a far smaller scale. I added that the ideal way in which this change could be effected would be for him, Sir Charles, to make the proposition at the United Board, for he was now President of the United Hospital.

Sir Charles Hyde declined to make the proposition in person, but he gave me sufficient encouragement for me to see several of the colleagues and business men interested in our hospital and within a few weeks there was formed the "Vernon Committee", with Mr. Sydney Vernon as its Chairman; this committee negotiated with several of the Special Hospitals, and eventually decided that the building could best be adapted as an Accident Hospital. This move has proved to be an outstanding success, though naturally the United Hospital did not like parting with a property valued at a hundred thousand pounds, with no assets in return.

CHAPTER V

THE MUNICIPAL HOSPITALS

UNTIL the early years of this century, the Infirmary in Dudley Road was chiefly occupied by chronic sick, a large proportion of whom needed nursing and medical supervision, but for whom there was no hope of cure. These "infirmaries" as they were called in this part of the world, were compelled by law to receive patients referred to them by the relieving officer. In those days, it was the Poor Law Authority, the Board of Guardians, who administered these institutions, and very few acute and curable cases ever came as in-patients. To the medical staffs, the work was relatively uninteresting, and although the Guardians did some very fine work in looking after the disabled veterans of industry, their popularity with the citizens generally was never at a high level; always they got more kicks than ha'pence from such publicity as they received.

It was not surprising, that when surgery more particularly outran the accommodation provided by the voluntary hospitals, and when it was obvious that by a variation in their staffs and equipment, they could make possible the filling-in of the deficiency in medical service, they should seize the opportunity with both hands.

During the Great War of 1914 to 1918, the Dudley Road Hospital was taken over by the military authorities and became the Second First Southern Hospital. For this purpose, it was largely altered and converted into an acute hospital, so that when it was returned to the city for civilian use in April, 1920, it was available for the treatment of acute civil cases. This was a fortunate circumstance, for it provided in the city beds sorely needed to supplement those of the two general hospitals, the General and the Queen's; both of these hospitals had very long waiting lists of patients, and there was no hope of clearing them without some assistance from elsewhere.

The Municipal Health Committee, who had now superseded Guardians, therefore held an informal conference with representatives of the University, of the Health Committee, and of the General and Queen's Hospitals, and avenues were explored with the hope that the staffs of the two general hospitals would be available to assist in staffing the Guardians' hospital; eventually, no *modus operandi* was found to be possible whereby all the staffs, and medical students (as asked by the voluntary staffs) could work at the municipal hospitals. The upshot was that in the main, the Guardians' hospital came to rely on whole-time officers in all subjects, though a few visiting specialists were appointed who were part-time officers.

From 1921 onwards, an increasing number of cases was accepted from the Voluntary Hospitals to be treated at the city hospitals. In the nine months of the first year,

679 cases were thus transferred, and for each of the years 1926-27, the number reached two thousand. Naturally the system whereby patients came in the first instance to the out-patient room to see a particular physician, and were then treated at another hospital by other officers, was by no means ideal. The practice of medicine is so much a personal matter that few patients want to be treated by "a" doctor; most of them want either their own practitioner, or someone recommended by him or their friends. Now under the Voluntary system, the close association of the consultants with the general practitioners in private practice, had led to the former having established a reputation in the first instance with the doctors, but soon with his patients as well.

Under the system used by the Guardians, the physicians and surgeons employed whole-time came rarely in contact with the general practitioners; their personalities were not known in the same way, and it took much longer to get to know their idiosyncrasies. Again, the control of admissions was entirely at the discretion of the Medical Superintendent, and the voluntary officers, who had been accustomed to assess the relative urgency of cases, found that they would now have no say in a matter which, to the Guardians, was a statutory obligation.

After three or four meetings, the conference faded out without any arrangement having been agreed, and from this stage onwards, the two groups of hospitals developed independently until the formation of the Hospitals Council once more brought together representatives of both groups.

The building of a new hospital at Selly Oak by the city authorities, and the taking over by the City Council of the duties which had hitherto been carried on by the Guardians, added greatly to the prestige of the municipal system, and the name "infirmary", for so long associated in this region with the poor-law system, was changed to that of "hospital". It thus appeared that the Municipal Hospitals were more and more rivalling the Voluntary Hospitals, and soon after the war ended, the equipment available at the Municipal Hospitals was much more up-to-date than that of either the General or the Queen's. The two latter institutions were suffering from the lack of funds so difficult to obtain on a voluntary basis in wartime, whilst the Municipal Hospitals, with the rates behind them, were not quite so heavily handicapped. Moreover, the Health Committee of the City Council was very much alive, and rightly did all it could to foster the growth and efficiency of its hospitals.

CHAPTER VI

THE MEDICAL SCHOOL AND THE UNIVERSITY

UP to the end of the eighteenth century, the usual way in which a student became a medical practitioner was to become apprenticed to a surgeon, and after a period of some four or five years, he set up in practice without any examination or registration. It is true that there were physicians who had passed examinations and who were University graduates, often in Arts as well as Medicine; these were the élite of the profession and were greatly esteemed on account of their high character and their attainments in scholarship. A large intermediate group of practitioners held the diplomas granted by the Society of Apothecaries (L.S.A.), or the College of Surgeons (M.R.C.S.). Of this group, the best were the hospital surgeons, though even here a diploma was not a necessary preliminary to appointment. The earlier surgeons of the General Hospital were simply members of the Surgeon's Company after apprenticeship, and wrote no letters after their names.

By the early days of the nineteenth century, those who aspired to become members of the new Royal College of Surgeons were required to take a course of study at a recognised school, and to pass an examination before the diploma was granted. So long as there was no examination for the majority of those going into practice, medical schools were unnecessary, and in the provinces, most men on receiving their articles went straight into practice. Slowly the standard of surgery was rising, and there grew up a series of Schools of Anatomy, which were patronised by all the best students. The earliest of such schools dated back to Cheseldon's in 1711, but when the College of Surgeons, in 1824, made attendance at a *hospital* school of anatomy obligatory, the private schools rapidly died out.

John Tomlinson, one of the first surgeons to the General Hospital and appointed in 1779, had already given a series of demonstrations and lectures on anatomy, and no doubt continued his instruction to the "cubbs" or apprentices to the surgeons at the General. No regular school was established in this city until 1825, when young William Sands Cox, on December the first of that year commenced his course of anatomical lectures, which was to be the forerunner of the Medical School. The lectures were first given at his house in Temple Row, where he practised surgery in partnership with his father. By 1826, he had received official recognition as a teacher of anatomy for the. L.S.A., and shortly afterwards for the M.R.C.S. For each of the first five years, the number of students attending classes was between 20 and 40, and from that period onwards, there has been no interruption in the courses of lectures, year by year.

In 1828, it was resolved to found a School of Medicine, as it was hoped that this course would avoid the year which all students sitting for the M.R.C.S. would otherwise be required to spend at a London school. "The distractions and allurements of the metropolis will not thus be prematurely presented to the young student". Cox appealed to the physicians and surgeons to the General Hospital to give lectures in their own subjects, and they cordially co-operated in forming a panel of lecturers.

In the next year, the school migrated from Temple Row to Snow Hill, Cox and his father being largely responsible for the cost of adjusting the building to their new requirements. This accommodation in turn became too small to house the lecture rooms and museum, and in 1834 Mr. E. T. Cox, the father of Sands Cox, bought a piece of land opposite the new Town Hall, then being built to the design of J. A. Hansom, the architect whose invention of the cab bearing his name is better known than his architecture. At that time, the land where now Queen's College stands was occupied by a derelict chapel, which was used as a carpenter's shop, and Cox senior paid only £1,500 for the site and buildings.

It is not necessary here to follow the fortunes of the school in detail; it needs only to be made clear that the school was so successful and became so popular that although the academic side of the work could be fully met at Queen's College, there was a deficiency in the clinical field available for the more practical work. For this reason, Sands Cox embarked upon his second and greatest adventure, which resulted in the building of the Queen's Hospital. It is remarkable that this was the only hospital in the country built in the first instance for the purpose of training medical students, and this purpose was "inherent in its constitution by virtue of its charter and statute". Its clinical character could only be altered by an Act of Parliament.

Most of Sands Cox's friends and supporters in this great enterprise were strong believers in a religious education being given to all students, and as Queen's College developed he was determined to make Queen's College the forerunner of a Central University. One by one, various departments were added, in Divinity, Arts and Science, but always there was a strong Anglican tendency. Indeed, in the 'fifties, when a formal Faculty of Theology was founded, and a supplementary charter was obtained, it became clear that all students, including medical students, were to be guarded from "the subtle designs of the Jesuits and the insidious intrusion of malignant dissenters" as had been advised in a letter from one of the main sub-scribers, the Rev. S. W. Warneford, LL.D., Rector of Bourton-on-the-Hill.

Gradually the clerical element gained more and more control over the affairs of the College and the Hospital, now comprising 140 beds; but the General Hospital surgeons now were finding it difficult to get apprentices, who were so valuable an asset to their hospital work, seeing that the General could not offer its students a complete academic and clinical course such as was now essential before they could obtain their diplomas. The staff of the General therefore started a rival school, named the "Sydenham School of Medicine", and the pre-clinical work was done in some buildings just opposite the hospital in Summer Lane. With two schools of medicine running side by side in Birmingham, students were free to choose, and in the 'fifties and 'sixties, the Queen's school, with the better accommodation, began to languish, whilst the Sydenham school, with poor rooms but greater freedom and directed by doctors with no clerical interference, was gradually collecting all the students of the neighbourhood. By the late 'sixties, the Queen's College was becoming insolvent, probably because too many new departments had been added, but to some extent because the somewhat rigid clerical control was unpopular in a town which contained many citizens who were professed Nonconformists. As the numbers of students fell away, Queen's College became more and more involved in financial troubles. Cox was accused by his colleagues on the council of being too headstrong, and of not having "those habits of business and exact regularity of temper and order so necessary to the administration of an institution". He had alienated the sympathy of his colleagues to such an extent that they asked him to resign. After an enquiry by the Charity Commissioners, a scheme was approved which was accepted by Parliament, whereby the College ceased to exercise any control over the Queen's Hospital, whose Governors now were to appoint the staff, who were to hold their offices subject to giving the students of Queen's College such clinical instruction as might be required by the examining boards.

The way was now clear for an amalgamation of the Queen's and Sydenham schools, for it was obvious that there was not room in Birmingham for two schools of medicine. In 1868, the Sydenham school was formally dissolved, and a new staff of professors and lecturers was agreed, to consist of an equal number of members of the General and Queen's medical staffs. There were of course some diehards, but the scheme was very successful, and soon the Birmingham Clinical Board was established to regulate the flow of students and to dovetail the clinical work at the two hospitals. The school steadily increased in numbers, and from accommodating 60 in 1868 reached 250 in 1890. At the same time, the Dental Act of 1881 made it important to provide for the development of a dental school, and the dental department, small for many years, was developed as part of the Faculty of Medicine. The Mason College was now built, with all the latest improvements for scientific training, and in 1892, the pre-clinical training in chemistry, physics and biology was transferred from Queen's College to the much better equipped laboratories in Edmund Street.

I have sketched out these developments which led up to the Medical School as we knew it in our student days, but I should be giving a false impression if my readers went away with the idea that they were easy, or were achieved without friction or heartburnings. The rivalry which had developed between the two hospitals at the time when Sydenham College was flourishing could not but leave some disturbance behind. In fact, over the years, the two hospitals gradually drifted apart, despite the Clinical Board which was common to both. The laymen on the respective governing bodies even more than the medical staffs tended to sort themselves out so that the General was conservative and the Queen's was liberal; perhaps it was because, having won its freedom from clerical control, and being determined never again to submit to non-medical domination, they valued their independence at the Queen's, whilst the General was content to keep its position as the oldest and the largest of the hospitals in Birmingham. Whatever the cause, the antagonism was very obvious at the time when, in 1906, I changed over from the smaller to the larger hospital, though it need hardly be stated that there were many members of both boards to whom these divergencies of political opinion meant nothing in comparison with the importance of administering the hospital to the best advantage. The influence of Dr. Bertram Windle was a powerful one in making for peace and development of the Medical School; in fact, it was during his deanship that most of the preparatory work was done which resulted in the school becoming the Faculty of Medicine of the University when the latter was established in 1900.

As the University expanded, it became clear that the building in the centre of the city at Mason College would soon become too small to accommodate all the faculties, and land at Edgbaston was acquired for the purpose in the first place of housing the Faculty of Science. Medicine which is in the pre-clinical stages so intimately associated with the sciences of chemistry, physics and biology, still remained in the Mason College building, and it was recognised that at some time in the not too distant future, it would be advisable to build a new Medical School in proximity to the other buildings on the Edgbaston site. It is true that other plans had been suggested, whereby the teaching should be retained in the centre of the town, at a place equally distant from both the rival general hospitals, but the Council of the University strongly favoured the union of all the faculties on the Edgbaston site, the move to take place as and when opportunity offered.

It may be interesting here to add a note as to the subsequent building of the Medical School, for although this housed the Faculty of Medicine, and was directly the concern of the University, the Appeal for funds for the Hospitals Centre included both the Hospital and the School; it was agreed that of the contributions made without any special reservation, one sixth should be allotted to the University for the Medical School, and the rest to the cost of constructing the hospital. As these two buildings were to be complementary and adjacent, the schedule as sent out for the competition by the selected architects included both buildings.

The School is a much smaller building than the Hospital; although building began on the former some twelve months later than at the hospital, it was ready for occupation nearly a year earlier.

All of the scientific services were arranged on the basis that they should be complementary, and every care was taken to avoid unnecessary overlapping in construction; it was hoped that the two managing committees, the Council of the University and the Board of the Hospital, would take advantage of the structural arrangements, and agree on the interlocking of the staffs of the two institutions. This process has in fact happened, and for practical purposes, all the staffs of the scientific ancillary

34

services of the hospital, now the Queen Elizabeth, are associated with the corresponding departments of the Medical School. Should other hospitals also be built on the adjacent sites, it is expected that a similar dovetailing of staffs will be arranged.

CARVING IN WALNUT IN FACULTY MEETING ROOM

CHAPTER VII

THE HOSPITALS COUNCIL

IN the early days of this century, the Voluntary Hospitals were to a very large extent supported by subscriptions from private sources, but increasingly by firms whose workpeople might be expected to become patients. Over the years since the Hospital Saturday Fund had been inaugurated, largely at the instance of Mr. Sampson Gamgee, the surgeon to the Queen's Hospital, there had been an increasing contribution from those who might be later accepted as patients, so that the hospitals, originally maintained solely as "charitable", were tending to become part of an insurance system against incapacity through illness. At the time of the outbreak of war in 1914, the charitable element was still a large factor making for a balance between income and expenditure, but the four years of the war period not only meant an increase in the cost of maintenance, but seriously diminished the income from the charitable group. As a result, all of the Voluntary Hospitals were running into debt, but they were so important a factor in the life of the nation, that at the end of the war, the Government set aside a sum of half a million pounds to be distributed among them.

For the purpose of making the allocation, a Commission was set up, and at the same time the opportunity was taken to carry out the recommendations of the earlier Cave Commission report. Local committees were formed and the one in Birmingham was known as the Voluntary Hospitals Committee; for a time, and until the allocation of funds had been made, this committee ran side by side with the Joint Hospitals Council, which was also interested in the Union Hospitals, later to be called the Municipal Hospitals.

The functions of these two committees may be summarised as follows:

Local Voluntary Hospitals Committee

(1) To act as local advisers to the Commission.
(2) To collect information as to the needs of the area.
(3) To further co-operation between hospitals.
(4) To advise as to a uniform system of accounts.
(5) To undertake the distribution of contributions made by local approved societies, and
(6) To assist hospitals to maintain the present voluntary system.

The Joint Hospitals Council

(1) To co-ordinate appeals.
(2) To consider the possibility of arranging transfer of patients.

(3) To prepare schemes of co-operative purchase.

(4) To organise systematic contributions from employers and employees.

After distribution of the government grant to the voluntary hospitals, it became possible to unite the two committees and thus avoid the overlapping so prevalent hitherto. The new body was called the Hospitals Council for the City of Birmingham. The constitution of the Council was as follows:

(1) The Lord Mayor.

(2) City Council nominees, the Chairman for the time being of the General Purposes, Mental Hospitals and Public Health Committees.

(3) Three representatives of the Medical Profession—two to represent the Consulting Physicians and Surgeons and one to represent the Panel Committee.

(4) Seven representatives to be nominated by the existing Joint Hospitals Council.

(5) The Hon. Secretary for the time being of the Hospital Saturday Fund.

(6) One representative of the Industrial Contributors to the Hospital Saturday Fund.

(7) One representative of the University.

(8) One woman.

(9) Commission nominees: Sir James Curtis, Mr. Alderman W. A. Cadbury, Councillor Miss H. Bartlett, Mr. William Hood.

In the spring of 1925, the amalgamation of the two bodies became effective, and the first Chairman was Sir Gilbert Barling.

It had been one of the conditions on which the various Voluntary Hospitals were awarded grants from the government fund that they should become members of the local Voluntary Hospitals Committee, and abide by its recommendations. It is correct to say that this was only a gentleman's agreement, but all hospitals regarded it as binding. One of the most important of the conditions which was laid down was that if any hospital contemplated any extension which would increase the number of its beds, they should notify the Hospitals' Council, in order that others should know what was projected. Another condition was that no public appeal for funds should be made without the prior consent of the Council, and it was in accordance with these undertakings that the General Hospital consulted the Council at various stages.

The first time a discussion took place that was to have an important affect upon the General Hospital Extension Scheme, was at the meeting of the earlier council in November, 1922. The General Hospital scheme was opposed by Alderman W. A. Cadbury on the ground that it would be much better to make all arrangements for the extension at a more suitable site in the suburbs, than to continue to extend locally. He put forward the proposal that the General and Queen's should agree on a scheme to cover the next 50 years, and that all extensions should be carried out on a new site, leaving the old hospital buildings to deal with casualties and out-patients, and a restricted number of ward cases. If a large site, say of 100 acres, could be obtained and reserved for hospitals, it would cost not much more than the sum the hospital would have to pay for the acre and a half they were contemplating buying on the St. Mary's site. If the General and Queen's completed their schemes as at present advocated, it would delay the purchase, and increase the cost, of a suitable site, which he envisaged as being able to accommodate in time all the Voluntary Hospitals of Birmingham, which might, as and when their present buildings had outlived their usefulness, rebuild on the new site.

I came across the notes I made of the meeting I attended and in which I replied to Alderman Cadbury. I agreed that if the new site could be in close proximity to the University, the building up of such a group of hospitals might well be an advantage. The greater space available would enable the patients to have a longer stay in hospital, and there would be much more room for later expansion as and when required. The fresh air argument was, I thought, of less importance today than before, and as smoke prevention became more effective, was likely to be even less of a determining factor.

There were, however, several points in which it was probable that the suburban hospital would be less useful than the urban one. The obvious one was that it would be necessary to maintain a duplicate system, with most if not the whole of the out-patients being seen at the urban site, and most of the in-patients treated at the suburban building. Such a dispersion was bound to be expensive, and would need a considerable increase in the medical staff; it would tend, too, to break the staff into two groups, and to destroy that corporate unity which meant so much in the tradition of a hospital. It would also result in the staff tending to get out of touch with the members of the City Council and those whose duty it was to direct other charitable agencies in the city, for at present, the visiting staff usually lunched at one or other of the clubs in the city and came into touch with members of the City Council and many of those in office in various public bodies.

Above all, my plea to go on with the local extension scheme was on the ground that it would take so long to get the agreement of the other hospitals, etc., and that our need for expansion was urgent.

I have given above the gist of the arguments used, but I was not able then to put forward one of the main reasons which I had in mind for obvious reasons. At the time in early 1920, when I first became interested in the hospital administration, I had toyed with the idea which was now put forward in more concrete form by Alderman Cadbury. One of my closest friends in the hospital world was Mr. William Billington, who was now one of the Honorary Surgeons to the Queen's Hospital, and who was to become the main driving force from the medical side in their extension scheme. I knew that I could safely discuss with him in private matters about which the two hospitals to which we were attached would not consult officially. We discussed whether it was possible, seeing that the staffs were so much more amicable now (1920) than they had been before the war, that the two hospitals would work together, and whether the other (special) hospitals would be likely to come into any agreed scheme. What we had in mind was a new suburban site,

38

with all the hospitals gradually migrating there and leaving only out-patient and casualty departments in the centre. Both of us made contacts with other hospitals to which we were consulting officers, but it soon became evident that such a scheme was not in the realm of practical politics. One of the chairmen to whom I tentatively broached the idea said it was out of the question, for that would mean they, his hospital, would become only a section of the General Hospital. It was obvious that the other institutions took the same view, and a very cautious sounding of a few of our own Committees of the General and Queen's made it certain that no suggestion of amalgamation, or even of a combined effort, would be acceptable. Those who have read the previous chapters, on the General and Queen's Hospitals will realise that the animosities of the nineteenth century still left their mark on the lay members of committee, even if the medical men had abated of their rancour.

With this background of experience, which I could not mention in the Council, it will not be a surprise that I considered the Alderman's proposal as a counsel of perfection which would take so long to bring to fruition that the General Hospital could not afford to wait, and I begged the Council to agree to our scheme being allowed to go forward, to complete the extension, and then, in a period of less urgency to try and work out the ideal for a suburban centre.

Eventually, the Hospitals Council suggested that the General Hospital should proceed with their negotiations, and as soon as their scheme was further advanced, they should bring it again before the Council. Thereafter, having obtained the approval of the other Voluntary Hospitals and the Hospital Saturday Fund officers, the Private Bill was promoted with the object of acquiring the St. Mary's site. By the time the Act of Parliament permitted us to buy the site, we were committed to an expenditure estimated at approaching £40,000, for the legal and professional expenses and the cost of clearing the site needed to be added to the sum paid for the land to the Ecclesiastical Commissioners.

It was only after the Act had been signed that a full-dress discussion of the position was again staged at the Hospitals Council. By this time, nearly all the preliminary work had been done, in so far as it devolved on the medical staff. Sketch plans had been made, the sizes of the various departments had been agreed, and their relative positions fixed, and the staff felt that after their long wait and the wearying work in many committees and sub-committees, they could see the buildings going up within a very few months. It came, therefore, as a very great surprise to the medical representatives of the General and Queen's, to learn that the opposition to their schemes which three years before had appeared to be confined to a few members of the Hospitals Council, now appeared to be the policy advocated by the very considerable majority of its members. There was a touch of the ludicrous given to the proceedings when our own House Governor, also a member of the Council in his official capacity, not only failed to support the scheme, but made it clear that he now preferred the alternative scheme for extension in the suburbs. Needless to say, no unanimous approval was forthcoming; the General Hospital, whose staff had watched with admiration not untinged with envy, the way in which the new ward blocks were going up at the rival Queen's Hospital, were disgusted with the way we had been encouraged to carry on with our scheme, only to be pulled up when we were committed to an expenditure of a large sum of money which the Hospital could ill spare and for which no return whatever had been obtained.

The actual resolution which was passed by the Hospital Council was proposed by Alderman Cadbury, and ran as follows:

"That no decision be taken on the proposal to extend the bed accommodation of the General Hospital in the centre of the city until full enquiry has been made through the Ministry of Health and other available sources as to the comparative cost and efficiency of general hospital extension in open suburban areas as compared with extension on central sites".

Neither Mr. Douglas Johnstone nor myself, the two members of our Extension Committee who were also on the Hospitals Council, had any doubt that although the order only said "halt", this was a fatal blow to the extension scheme; the defection of our House Governor, which neither of us had expected, was itself a mortal blow, and the whole tone of the discussion in the Council made it certain that now the scheme was stone dead and the whole of our five years of arduous work was wasted.

CHAPTER VIII

THE GRANT ROBERTSON COMMITTEE

AFTER the collapse of the General Hospital Extension Scheme, I assumed that I had finished with all committee work which would deal with such extensions as were necessary to our hospital; more out of curiosity than hope, I remained a member of the Hospitals Council, intending to retire as soon as my term as representative of the consultants had expired. It was a great relief to get back to practice, both in private and at the hospital, and once more be able to devote a reasonable time to the teaching of students.

A few months after the débâcle, the Hospitals Council took the initiative in setting up what was afterwards known as the "Grant Robertson Committee". The reference was as follows:

"That the Governing bodies of the General and Queen's Hospitals be requested to meet and consider the outlines of a scheme for a new Hospitals Centre, on the assumption that an adequate site adjacent to the University will be available— the basis in the first instance being that the minimum number of general hospital beds in the city by 1931 should be not less than 2,400, and to submit their recommendations to this sub-committee in due course".

The two hospitals accepted the invitation, and after consultation set up a committee consisting of two lay and two medical members from each governing body; the two house governors; and the only member common to both the Board of Management of the General and the Committee of the Queen's, Mr. Charles Grant Robertson, the Principal of the University.

I had hoped to be excused this committee work, but my colleagues on the Medical Committee of the General pressed me to be one of their nominees, as I already had so wide a knowledge of the needs of our hospitals. As it was evident that the call upon my time would not be extensive, I accepted on condition that it did not commit me to any further work of that character.

The Committee was constituted as follows:

For the General Hospital—	For the Queen's Hospital—
Mr. E. P. Beale,	Mr. W. E. Adlard,
Mr. Owen W. Thompson,	Mr. H. F. Keep,
Mr. L. P. Gamgee,	Mr. W. Billington,
Dr. Stanley Barnes, and	Dr. J. G. Emanuel, and
Mr. A. E. Leaney (House Governor).	Mr. G. Hurford (House Governor).

Principal Grant Robertson was nominated by both hospitals.

This committee, called for short the "Grant Robertson Committee" was composed entirely of Voluntary Hospital men. With the exception of the two House Governors of the General and Queen's, all were members of the Board of Management of the General or of the Committee of Management of the Queen's. The only member common to both hospitals was the Principal of the University, Charles Grant Robertson, who had been appointed to the hospital committees as a link between the two teaching hospitals and the Medical School which was now the Faculty of Medicine of the University. It was therefore natural that he should be appointed as Chairman, and it was he, of course, who drew up the report which was thereafter called by his name.

The Grant Robertson Report is a document of some length, the preliminary section being designed to indicate why certain resolutions were adopted. The summary is as follows:

(1) That the new Hospital Centre to be established on a site adjoining the University at Edgbaston should not be an independent institution, but should be under the joint control of the General and Queen's Hospitals.

(2) That with this object it would be of the greatest advantage that the General and Queen's Hospitals should be amalgamated for all purposes.

(3) That the amalgamation of the two hospitals recommended in Resolution No. 2 at as early a stage as possible would minimise the difficulties in the creation of the new Hospital Centre.

(4) That the unified Board of Management for the new Hospital Centre, the General and the Queen's Hospitals at the outset should have at their disposal a minimum of 1,200 beds.

(5) That in view of fundamental considerations to which the Committee attach the greatest importance, and which are briefly explained in the appropriate paragraphs of this report, the new Hospital Centre should start with a minimum of 750 beds.

The report was signed by every member.

The discussions had lasted for some six months, and it was noticeable that none of the acrimony that might have been expected when representatives of the two rival hospitals met, was present at these meetings. Perhaps it was that so many of us medical men had served on both hospitals; Gamgee, senior surgeon at the General, was the son of the famous Queen's surgeon, Sampson Gamgee, of "Gamgee Tissue" and Hospital Saturday fame. Most of my training had been at the Queen's, and I had been resident and pathologist there for a total of over five years, while Emanuel had been pathologist at the General and was now senior physician at the Queen's. The other medical man was Billington, who had also done a large amount of his early work at the General, and was now senior surgeon at the Queen's. No doubt, it was also due to the fact that the lay representatives were not of those who had been associated with previous disputes between the two teaching hospitals.

When we had finished our last meeting and agreed the Report, most of us felt that there was very little chance of its being translated into bricks and mortar. We had been asked to produce an ideal plan and we had produced it. We had not been asked how much it would cost, as this was largely a medical committee, but Gamgee and I could both give fairly close estimates of costs by this time, and we agreed that if we allowed a quarter of a million for the Medical School, the overall cost would be in the region of a million. I did not ask what Emanuel thought, but Billington, who knew more about finance than most business men, agreed with our estimates. I never knew what Grant Robertson thought the cost might be, as at that time I did now know him well.

The Grant Robertson Report was approved unanimously by the Board of the General Hospital on September 24th, 1926, and went to the Hospitals Council on October 14th, when it received general approval; several members made the reservation that it might prove too costly, and the Council set up a committee to consider the finance of the scheme. I have no notes as to their report, and was, as a medical man, not a member of the committee.

Like the Hospitals Council, the Press received the Report with acclamation, but as expected made reservations as regards cost. Both Gamgee and I assumed that we had now finished with the development of our hospitals; he, because he was due shortly to retire from the active staff of the General, and I, because I had spent so much time on administrative work that I might now be allowed to get back to what I regarded as my essential work, the practice of medicine.

I was now free to return to my work as a neurologist, and once more to attend committees only when it was convenient, and when it did not clash with my real work. I still attended the Medical Committees of the General Hospital, and such of the board meetings as might have a bearing on our medical work; and I remained a member of the Hospitals Council, as my term of office as a representative of the consultants had not yet expired. Chiefly I attended all these meetings out of curiosity, to see what measures would be suggested for relieving at the two general hospitals a situation which was rapidly becoming intolerable. I took no active part in any of the discussions, and was prepared to be a spectator and to watch how the others got out of the difficulties.

Within a few months of the collapse of our extension scheme, the Hospitals Council, at the request of Alderman W. A. Cadbury, arranged for deputations to visit various continental hospitals of renown; Mr. and Mrs. Cadbury, accompanied by Dr. J. G. Emanuel, Mr. H. H. Sampson, Mr. J. B. Leather and Mr. A. H. Leaney visited among other places Copenhagen and Hamburg, and investigated how the hospitals there were built and maintained. They later brought their comments to the Council in the form of a report, printed in May, 1927; the whole of the expenses of the tours and the report were met by Mr. Cadbury.

One of the unexpected items in the report was that the pavilion system of building "is costly to build and to heat, and very expensive to administer". A notable departure from English practice was the very large amount of ancillary room left available near the wards, a form of building which we eventually adopted for the Queen Elizabeth Hospital. Yet another departure from our usual practice was the greater sub-division of the wards into smaller units, for only rarely did a ward contain as many as 20 beds, and the usual maximum was 12.

Other visits were paid by various members of the staff and of the administration, Dr. K. D. Wilkinson brought back information about hospitals in Australia, Professor Billington about Glasgow, and a visit by Mr. A. H. Leaney was followed by a fairly full report of conditions in American hospitals. At a later stage, all these reports were to be used in determining how we should proceed to design our new hospital (see Appendix, page 135).

CHAPTER IX

ITEMS IN THE GRANT ROBERTSON REPORT

IT will be convenient here to give some of the reasons why the various items were put forward in the Grant Robertson Report. When the Executive Board of the Hospitals Centre was afterwards set up, the pros and cons were again discussed in detail, but to avoid re-iteration, the gist of the various reasons may well be given now.

This was to be a Medical School Hospital, in the sense that all students of the Faculty of Medicine of the University should have access to it, and that the various teachers of clinical subjects should have places on the staff of the hospital. One of the chief difficulties from which the school of medicine in this city had suffered for fifty years, was the dispersion of the various clinical units; in their third, fourth and final years, the students might be required not only to attend lectures at Edmund Street, but to visit the General or the Queen's Hospitals; at some times, he would also be required to attend the Mental Hospital at Winson Green or elsewhere, to go to a fever hospital in yet another district, and at times to attend at the Eye Hospital or the Ear and Throat Hospital. His midwifery was learned either at the Queen's or at Loveday Street. This degree of dispersion meant that the student might be faced with so much travelling from one place to another that much time was lost that should have been devoted to study, whilst the administrators of the school found it difficult to keep track of individual students, and be sure that they were using the time available to the best advantage.

To the medical members of the Grant Robertson Committee, these facts were well known, and of course the Principal on many occasions had heard of the difficulties of administering such a diffusion of students' work. It therefore was natural that the committee should have constantly in mind that this new hospital should eventually be *the* medical school general hospital when all the changes projected had been made, to the exclusion of the existing general hospitals. The medical members of the committee also made it clear that they were not prepared to participate in any scheme for the building of a new hospital, unless it were located in immediate proximity to the Medical School of the University. We knew that these views were also shared by those who directed University policy, and that they had in mind the removal to Edgbaston of the Faculty of Medicine, now in Edmund Street in the Mason College building. So far as the medical members of the committee were concerned, they would only consent to be active agents in the creation of a new hospital which must reduce the status of those to which they had been appointed, and of which they were rightly proud, if the new hospital was built on such a scale and in such a position, that it satisfied these requirements.

Although we had had the advantage of receiving the report of Sir James Curtis and Sir John Robertson, in which they had estimated the bed shortage in Birmingham in 1926 at from six to eight hundred, some of us were constantly, both in this period and later, trying to form an estimate of the bed deficiency. We, at the Centre, were only interested in the beds for "acute" cases; where chronic cases are being treated, the demands on the staff and especially on the ancillary services, will be on a much smaller scale, and it will never be economic to use a hospital deliberately built for acute cases, for chronic cases who may need a prolonged stay in the hospital.

So far as my memory serves me, we never had a formal discussion on this subject at the Executive Board. At a later stage, and even after the hospital was built, I had to put my ideas into more concrete form, when acting as a surveyor for the Nuffield Trust in Northern Ireland. For the sake of those readers who may have little knowledge of the ways in which this question is tackled, it may be of advantage to put down on paper how the figures are computed, and to indicate how it comes about that so much difference of opinion can be expressed by those whose duty it is to make sure that there is no shortage of beds.

From the point of view of the patient and his relatives, beds are too few if he is required to wait for more than a few days for admission, once in-patient treatment has been agreed. It is a hardship for a man with hernia or a child with enlarged tonsils to be kept waiting for an operation for more than a week or two at the outside, for the period of waiting may mean the development of complications, and there is the added anxiety inseparable from an impending operation. If, as was often happening in 1932 here, such a patient had to wait for a time measured in months or even years, it is obvious that severe shortage exists. Some of the reasons given by relatives may have no real bearing on this question, as they are asking the "acute" hospital to take in an unsuitable patient—not because the patient is not ill, but because the acute hospital is not the one to which he should be admitted; it is not right, for instance, to admit cases who cannot take advantage of the very expensive staff and equipment of the acute hospital, when it is known that no treatment they can give will save life, and when proper accommodation should be provided elsewhere. It should not be expected that a patient slowly dying of disseminated cancer, or in the later stages of senility, should be housed in our acute hospital excepting in so far as some special treatment may there be given which might not be available elsewhere to alleviate some symptom.

Many cases are admitted as urgencies; they take precedence over all other cases, and should be admitted in this way solely for medical reasons; as all of us are human, there is bound to be some error in such admissions, and pressure is often put upon the staff to admit particular cases for social reasons. Whoever has to decide this point, there is certain to be heartburning when beds are short, but it is my experience that the medical officer who is put in charge of admission of cases makes the best choice; admission through the administration office is likely to be less successful in admitting the right type of patient.

For the purpose of a general hospital being able to admit urgencies, some beds must always be available. The patient brought to the Casualty, with a bruised head and smelling of alcohol, may have fallen and hurt his head because he had some brain disease like apoplexy, and some kindly stranger had given him a nip of brandy to tide him over the arrival of the ambulance. On the other hand, of a hundred such cases arriving at the hospital, only a very small proportion will be suffering from anything worse than drunkenness, and if the resident officer admits all of them, he will be likely to be reprimanded by his chief for filling much wanted beds with "drunks"; yet even the most expert cannot be sure at a first examination which diagnosis is correct, even with an X-ray examination, and if the recently qualified house-surgeon makes a mistake, he is likely to hear some very caustic remarks from the coroner.

For such cases, there must be observation beds available, in which such a patient may be kept for one or two days; by this time, the diagnosis can be made with reasonable certainty, but this means that to keep such beds available, there must be some beds empty, thus swelling the list of "unoccupied beds".

There is always a tendency for dust—which may contain bacteria or spores—to accumulate on walls, ceilings and ward furniture. Every year, each ward should undergo a thorough "spring cleaning", preferably with a fresh distempering of walls and ceilings; in order to minimise the shortage difficulty thus caused, such closing down of beds is always done in summer, when the pressure is at its lowest.

For technical reasons, a general hospital is divided up into several groups; it would obviously be wrong to put a maternity case into a medical women's ward, and *vice versa*. Again, some of the cases belong to the "specialties", and they cannot be mixed up with the other cases for technical reasons; neither the nurses nor the medical staff would be adaptable for such an arrangement.

When, in an acute hospital, allowance has been made for all of these difficulties of accommodation, it is usually found that the occupancy level in a well-run acute general hospital is about eighty-five per cent. The figure will be higher in the winter and lower in the summer.

If beds are short from the point of view of the admitting officers, they try to eke out their bed-supply chiefly in two ways. Let us assume that all available space has otherwise been used, that the patient's day-rooms and the rooms allotted to those officers and servants who *can* live out, have been taken up for patients' beds. By putting up extra beds in the wards, the complement can be increased; often I have seen as many as four mattresses—without bedsteads—on the floor of a main ward, on which patients are nursed and treated. The medical staff are always apprehensive that such a degree of overcrowding may result in a spread of infection; the nursing staff hate such expedients, for not only is their work correspondingly increased, but it is much more difficult to nurse a patient in such a lowly position.

The second method is to send out patients at an earlier stage than is normal. If, instead of keeping a patient in hospital for an average, say, of twenty days, the average becomes eighteen days, then the capacity of the hospital for dealing with patients is increased by some ten per cent.

This system is bad for everyone concerned. The patient is prematurely released from the discipline of the hospital, so necessary in his eating, drinking and smoking; it is particularly dangerous if he exerts himself at too early a stage. It is obviously bad for a harassed housewife with little accommodation and several little children to look after, if she now has added the care of an only partly recovered husband. It is bad for the medical staff, for they know that their reputation will suffer if anything goes wrong, even if they have disclaimed responsibility for the patient after he has left the hospital. It is worst of all for the nursing staff, for it means that they have an abnormal proportion number of cases acutely ill at the same time, and there is no relief such as they may expect from having some patients who are approaching the convalescent stage.

Both these methods of dealing with shortage of beds are bad, but they are practically the only ones available in times of emergency. It follows that when we are trying to estimate our need for more beds it will be no answer to say "I went round the XYZ Hospital yesterday, and found that no less than twenty beds were empty". Unfortunately, this argument has been brought forward again and again.

Wherever the plans described above have needed to be adopted, we can be sure that there is a shortage of beds, but it is a much more difficult problem to decide how many are required to make up the deficiency. The method we adopted at the General Hospital in estimating our needs in 1921, depended largely on the "waiting lists". These were the names of patients who had been seen in the out-patient room or elsewhere by members of the staff, and who were judged to be in need of in-patient treatment, but whose condition was not so urgent that admission must be at once or not at all. As each bed on an average represented about twenty patients a year, we could get an idea of the quantitative shortage from this figure.

Another group of figures had to be brought into this account. In the years immediately succeeding the First Great War, we were sending elsewhere a large number of urgent cases, who should have priority in admission on account of the type of illness; such would include acute appendicitis, pneumonia, operable cancer, etc., and a considerable number of such casualties as fractured thighs. In all of these urgencies, in-patient treatment must be provided at once, and at this period we were sending to other institutions anything up to two thousand cases a year—all urgent.

Naturally this method of assessing the deficiency is imperfect; for whenever the waiting lists got so long that an absurd time elapsed before admission was possible, the patients made their way elsewhere; when things got really bad, some had died before they could be admitted and many others had gone elsewhere for treatment that was denied to them at our hospital. Indeed, some patients, in a despairing

48

effort to get a tonsillectomy or an operation for hernia performed, had put their names down for two or more hospitals, and had ceased to need admission to our hospital when their turn had come.

Today (1952), a method of assessing the shortage is to compare our own numbers of beds for various types of patient with those of comparable cities in this or other countries. This means of gauging our deficiencies was not of sufficient accuracy in the years immediately succeeding the First Great War, as so many extra beds of varying types were set up as "temporary", and the distinction between the various types—acute, chronic and special—was not sufficiently indicated in the records that were available. Although such figures were not at our disposal in 1930, it may be of interest to note that the ones given by various surveyors for the Nuffield Trust in the period between 1941 and 1943, showed that the total number of general hospital beds for the whole country, including chronic but excluding infectious, was 225,000; the summary in the "Domesday Book of the Hospital Services" adds that "this figure needs to be increased by 40 per cent."

A fairly generally accepted figure for overall hospital provision in this country, exclusive of those for mental disease, is now ten beds for every thousand of the population, and of these about half will be for acute work, including the specialties. I believe the figures for Canada and the United States are somewhat higher, and those for London are higher than for any of the other cities in England.

When Gray and Topping made their survey of the hospital services in London in 1945, they concluded that the provision for inhabitants of the County of London, and excluding those beds occupied in London by those from other areas, was, for each thousand: "General acute, 6.3; Maternity, 0.71".

They stated that at the time of the survey, these figures must be taken as showing a deficiency. In another paragraph, they note, "Any exact measure of adequacy of the hospital services, whether in quantity or quality, is almost impossible, since a number of factors enter in, many of which are intangible".

A similar review of the position in Birmingham was made for the Nuffield Trust by Hunter, Veitch Clark and Hart in 1945. In their opinion "There was evidence. . . . of insufficiency or at least lack of availability of beds in certain categories, and of maldistribution of beds in relation to population density and local demands for in-patient treatment".

There never will be a figure agreed by all members of our democracy. It will be determined by such variables as our financial capacity, our standard of housing, our degree of civilisation and our social conscience. The proportion of beds needed today (1952) is higher than it was in 1931, not that there is any more disease to combat, but because of the variation in the intangible factors.

In a city like Birmingham, the centre of a large manufacturing area in which live some two and a half million people, the provision we have to make for hospital work will depend to a considerable extent upon the adequacy of the services in the adjacent and nearby towns and villages. If these are on such a scale and of such a

49

professional standard that they have earned the confidence of their citizens, then the overall figure for our city excluding beds for mental disease, need not greatly exceed the average of ten beds per thousand; of these five will be allotted to acute work, including the specialties.

CHAPTER X

THE SIZE OF THE HOSPITAL

THE instruction to the Grant Robertson Committee from the Hospitals Council was to the effect that we should put forward what we considered to be an ideal scheme for satisfying a bed deficiency of 600 to 800. Verbally it was made clear that these beds were to be for acute cases of the type that we had been accustomed to receive as patients at the General and Queen's Hospitals, and that this new provision was to substitute the extension schemes of the General and Queen's. It was also made clear that what was required was a hospital suitable for medical education.

In the discussion which follows, it should be understood that no provision was to be made for chronic cases, who would only be admitted for short periods as necessity arose; for infectious fevers, for whom the city authorities were responsible; or for mental disease, which again was a municipal concern and for which at a later date provision was expressly excluded in the lease from the Calthorpe estate.

At various stages, both in the Grant Robertson Committee and in the later Executive Board of the Hospitals Centre, the question as to the size of the hospital to be built, was discussed time after time; it became one of the most hotly argued points when the controversy arose in 1931, and continued to be argued till the decision of the Lord Mayor's Committee in 1932. It would be tedious to repeat at each stage what was argued, so although the arguments were spread over some years, I will set them out here as though they were decided at a single occasion.

One of the first questions to be answered was this. Could we start to build by putting up a complete hospital of 300 beds, and then bit by bit, as more beds became necessary, add various ward blocks and the necessary auxilliary and ancillary services? I confess that I was strongly opposed to this idea when first the Grant Robertson Committee met in 1927, for I had already had four years of experience in discussing with architects and engineers how we could expand and modernise the General Hospital in Steelhouse Lane.

To start with a small hospital of 300 beds would have been a much easier project, for it would have silenced most of our critics, and needed a much smaller sum of money. Had we been building a home for chronic patients, where nursing rather than medical attention was the predominant factor, such a plan would have been feasible. When the time came to expand, an extra ward block could be put up, if land for that purpose had been left available, and a wing could be added to the nurses' home; the only other services which would need expansion were the auxilliary services, kitchens, heat, light, power, water supply and drainage. All these could be so arranged as to be in their right places in a hospital double the size of the original 300 beds.

Even in a special hospital, some similar provision might be made, for here, the only extras beyond those already mentioned would be an addition to the out-patient department, and to a small number of ancillary services. An entirely different position exists in the acute general hospital and especially if it is a medical school hospital. Here there must be a large number of ancillary services, such as bacteriology, bio-chemistry, clinical pathology, dentistry, physio-therapy and above all X-rays, and these must, for the hospital to carry out its duties at the highest level, be in the right place and of sufficient size to allow of some degree of expansion and variation in internal arrangements to meet the developments of medical practice. Above all, the clinical rooms where students are taught, and any lecture rooms must be of the size ultimately required, for it is impossible to divorce these rooms from the hospital itself. Those who have tried so to alter a committee room designed to hold, say twenty people, and then suddenly find that forty is the number now required in the expanded building, will realise how difficult is such a single adaptation. I must have argued this question with a dozen of my architect friends before we met in the Grant Robertson Committee, to try and find out whether some new form of building might not be put up in such a way that it could be expanded in, say, ten years' time; none of them could suggest a way which was reasonably economical, and which would not make the primary 300 bed hospital less efficient.

I have said nothing here of two departments which would obviously be necessary, but for which accommodation might be arranged in the purlieus and precincts of the hospital, rather than within the walls which contained the ward blocks. Most house governors will wish that their offices shall be in the closest association with the wards, and it is even more desirable that the resident medical officers shall be on call immediately if an emergency should arise, as so frequently happens in an acute hospital. With good planning in the first instance, all these services can be located in the right places; but a majority will not be expansible, for to operate at a high level of efficiency, they will often need to be squeezed in between wards or some other important rooms.

Another suggestion that was discussed at a later stage, after the Grant Robertson Committee had reported, and after its recommendations had been accepted by the Hospitals Council, was that a 300-bed hospital should be put up on the Centre site, and that the other 300 beds might be set up in the north-east of the city at, say, Kingstanding. Such a plan was advocated by many of those who lived away from the Centre site, on the grounds that it would be much nearer to the patients' homes, that the relatives would have easier access to their sick friends, and that some degree of local patriotism might develop in the more homely atmosphere of the smaller institution. So far as the first point was concerned, we saw little merit in the argument when we considered the question of transport. Although in the days of horse-drawn traffic it was a matter of importance to get the journey over quickly for the patient, in the days when motor ambulances were freely available, as we anticipated they soon would be, the worst time for the patient is not in the actual journey but in the getting in and getting out. As the ambulance drive could, at most, only be increased by some twenty minutes, this part of the argument could only influence our decision if other things were equal.

The second point, that the relatives would have longer distances to travel, and higher fares to meet, also seemed of little moment. Again, the extra time occupied would be less than half an hour, and we were prepared to trust to the almoners or some body like the Charity Organisation Society, to see that the fare was no hardship to the relatives. The third point, as to the development of local patriotism was, of course, more important to a voluntary hospital. Although the purely "charitable" funds had ceased to be the chief sources of money required for maintenance, yet the esteem in which a hospital is held by the people it serves is a very potent factor in its progress. All of us on the earlier committees had served in some capacity on a voluntary hospital, and all of us gave full weight to this argument; but when we came to analyse what it meant in other directions, we rejected the idea almost unanimously.

One other line of argument was put forward. It was said by some that whereas in a 300-bed hospital, the sense of homeliness and of personal interest in the welfare of the individual patients was maintained at a high level, these very valuable human touches would be lost in a 600-bed institution. At the later stages of the controversy, this point recurred again and again, but I confess that I cannot see why the difference should exist. As we all know, medicine is a very personal subject, and the more the idiosyncrasies and personal wishes of the patient are satisfied, the greater will be his appreciation of the service given. He will be happier with a less efficient treatment, of whose defects he will probably never be conscious, if the attitude of those nurses and doctors who look after him, is one of personal interest and kindly care. Surely, this attitude of the staff to the patient is not dependent on the total numbers in the hospital; it is the business of the heads of departments, managerial, nursing and medical, to see that their officers act as they should in dealing with their patients. The much derided "bedside manner" is one of the most important of those personal approaches to a patient, and is just as likely to be absent in a small as in a large hospital.

Yet another argument was put forward to try and turn us from the 600-bed hospital we were contemplating; it was said that it was impossible to manage properly a hospital of this size. I am afraid that this argument left most of us cold. We pointed out that there were many other hospitals in this country and abroad, where numbers larger than 600 were accommodated, and where there was no evidence of difficulty in management. In any case, our reply was that the hospital was to be built essentially for patients, and that even if it proved to be a little more difficult to administer than a smaller one, that fact ought not to stand in the way of our advocating the larger unit. The administration must accommodate itself to the patient's needs, and not *vice versa*.

The overwhelming arguments for a large single unit came from the medical school angle. We assumed that there would be built, as there now has been built by the University, a medical school in the immediate vicinity of the acute general hospital. The new hospital was to be the substitute for the extension schemes of the General and Queen's, at which medical students would be taught their clinical work. Looking forward, say twenty years, not long in the life of a hospital, what would be the position of a hospital of 300 beds four or five miles away at Kingstanding? Would it be able to maintain its position as a medical school hospital? Most of us were certain that the students would use every device to become clerks and dressers at the hospital near the medical school, for this course would not only avoid the extra hour of travelling to and fro, which would be a daily journey; they would find themselves divorced from those teachers, like the professors of medicine and surgery, who were certain to be located at the hospital near the medical school. The time would come, and come quickly, when the University would say that it was no longer possible to train students so far away; in addition, one of the main reasons why the new medical school was to be built at the Centre was that the services, especially the ancillary services, would be complementary; such would be impossible at the distant hospital.

One other reason for the larger unit was of even more technical importance; it was the existence within the hospital walls of special departments. Quite naturally, those representatives of the special hospitals on the Executive Board, could never agree that their hospitals were not a sufficient answer to our problem. Quite rightly, they had great pride in the Eye, the Ear and Throat, the Orthopaedic, the Skin, and other voluntary hospitals that had been built over the previous century. We, who had to look after the medical student's education, never managed to convince the special hospital members that we must, in our general hospital, include such specialties as they had already provided for the city. Why, they said, do you not send the students to our hospitals? Their staffs were of consultant standard, or at least most of them were. That was not our trouble.

In the course of his education, the student must learn something of all the "specialties"; these will include those mentioned above, but there must be added fevers, to be learned, so far as our students were concerned, at the fever hospital three miles away; mental disease, usually five miles away, and tuberculosis, three miles from the school we were expecting to be built. Add up what this meant in travelling to the medical student in his later years of training, and it will be found that there will be no time left for the still more important subjects of medicine, surgery, gynaecology and midwifery.

Those of us who had had experience of the teaching of students over the years, and more especially the deans of the Faculty of Medicine whose duty it was to organise this teaching, knew that the modern development of specialisation needed a radical change in our hospital arrangements if the students were to be properly equipped for their work as general practitioners in the future.

There was another reason why we, in the new general hospital we were building, wanted so many of the specialities to be housed under one roof. The human body cannot be segregated into a series of separate compartments. All "special" types are interdependent to a varying degree. Take for instance the eye; although eye work is a very specialised type of surgery, many of the diseases that occur in the eye are due to such conditions as high blood-pressure, diabetes or heart disease, and it may often happen that the eye trouble is only an index, though usually a most important one, of disease elsewhere. Again, in a general hospital, where all sorts of abnormal conditions are being treated, it is a frequent happening that some complication in a "specialty" occurs. How are they to be dealt with? Now it is one of the troubles of specialisation that the more it develops, the less do the other doctors see of the specialty, and the time comes when they are so far out of touch with it that they are no longer prepared to take the responsibility of treating such cases.

To meet this situation in the early days of this century, most general hospitals appointed "consulting" ophthalmologists, and similar visiting consultants in other subjects, while the "special" hospitals in the same way appointed "consulting" physicians and surgeons to deal with any non-special work which should arise. As a rule, the officer selected for the consulting position was the most eminent of those available, and usually, he was so busy that it was a matter of great difficulty for him to find time to visit another hospital beyond one or two to which he was already attached. The delays, and the difficulty of arranging personal consultations between the principals concerned, made this method only partly successful, and many of us who had been active agents in this way, longed to see some better way of re-organising the work. Indeed, many of the older hospital officers attached to the general hospitals, remained actively hostile to any further development of specialisation, though the public, and even more the press, made it impossible to maintain the position of the physician or surgeon who still desired to remain general in the sense of fifty years ago.

Granted that we were to accept specialisation, as most of us did, what was the best way in which we could adapt a modern hospital to make the greatest use of it? We had heard of places abroad where specialisation had run so wild that no doctor would admit that he was a general practitioner, and it had become the duty of the patient himself to decide which specialist he should attend. Clearly, if the specialists were to be of maximum help, they must be closely associated with those practising other branches of medicine and surgery. Our conclusion was that we must set up departments of our own in the new general hospital, if we were to provide the "ideal" hospital we were instructed to put forward to the Hospitals Council.

The only condition on which we were prepared to abandon a special department in the general hospital, was that the corresponding special hospital should be built in close proximity, so that at any time, day or night, a consultation could be easily arranged, and so that there would be a real consultation where the principals of the two hospitals could meet. At the moment, and until the general hospital of the Centre was in being, it was impossible to dispense with the special departments; we therefore decided to build on the assumption that we should need accommodation for special departments in Dentistry, Ophthalmology, Ear and Throat, Gynaecology and Maternity, and Dermatology.

For one other type many of us were concerned to see that provision was available. I have noted before how urgent was the requirement at the General Hospital that had to be made for casualties, including more particularly the damages from accident. The increasing use of motor traffic on the roads, and the continued development of power in the factories to replace muscular effort, was increasing the accident rate every year, and whenever a hospital improved its accommodation and its service to meet the demand, it was swamped by the immediate increase in the numbers sent in. We all agreed that provision should be made for all casualties to be treated as near to where the accident arose as possible, and as the group of factories on the south-west of the city only constituted a third of those in Birmingham, a moderate provision must be made or developed on or near our Centre site as well as a much larger one on a site nearer the north-east than the south-west. If we were to be a complete general hospital, it was of course necessary to have a casualty department, but as it was possible to develop one at the General Hospital in Steelhouse Lane, we felt that for the time, by arrangement with the police and the ambulance service, we need not make any special arrangements for casualties at Edgbaston. In fact, when we started actual building, we omitted altogether the casualty, and within a few years had managed to make even better arrangements than were possible for us in '33; the whole of the Queen's Hospital was handed over to a special committee, who there set up the Accident Hospital which has done magnificent service. As this hospital is less than a mile from the Queen Elizabeth, there should be no necessity to institute a department for casualties there in the near future.

Once we had accepted the decision to establish special departments, it became important to decide how large each must be, if it were to be an effective unit. As the "consulting" system had failed to give ideal results, we needed to have officers of special departments attached to our hospital alone, instead of their loyalty and work being divided among a series of hospitals. If we were to build our new hospital on such a plan, each special officer must have a department of his own which would be of sufficient size, in both in-patient and out-patient work, to occupy all the time he could spare from private practice. We did not want him to be attached to any other special hospital.

The appointment of a single officer as head of such a department automatically means that he must have a junior, partly that he may be in training to take the senior position if he succeeds, and partly to substitute his senior if the latter should, through illness, vacation or other cause, not be available. In addition, there would need to be a house-officer in residence, and if the department were of any great size, a registrar as well.

The upshot is that each department must be of a certain minimal size to be fully effective; and when we added together all the space necessary to accommodate the special departments, it became obvious that they would swamp the essential departments of medicine and surgery in a 300-bed hospital.

Here was yet another argument which reinforced our determination to build on the 600 basis rather than the 300.

Yet another suggestion was introduced by one of the members. Why not build a 300-bed hospital at Edgbaston, and locate there all the whole-time professors, with charge of practically all the beds? Such a solution would fail, as most of us thought, for several reasons. How long would it be before it was called "The University Hospital", and how long would it be before the staff there were accused of using the hospital for the purpose of experimenting on their patients? A further reason against this plan was that the academic urge to be derived from the whole-time professors and their staffs, would be largely lost if they were divorced from the rest of the teaching staff by being located at a separate hospital. Of course, the students would use every endeavour to clerk and dress at the professorially staffed hospital, for then their teachers would also be the examiners who would decide whether they qualified. Finally, the overwhelming argument against such a hospital was that there were no funds from which such a professorial staff could be paid; and in 1927 there was no indication that such funds would be forthcoming.

Many of the arguments I have put forward here were discussed in the Grant Robertson Committee; they continued to crop up in print or in committee until the final decision was taken four years later.

———————

CHAPTER XI

AMALGAMATION OF THE GENERAL AND QUEEN'S HOSPITALS

IF the new hospital should come under the control of the two hospitals concerned in its design and construction, we could see no way in which it could be effectively managed without the amalgamation of the General and Queen's for all purposes. We were acutely conscious that this would be a most formidable and thorny question in view of the history of the two institutions over the previous century. Those of us on the Grant Robertson Committee had naturally been chosen to some extent because as individuals we should be able to work with our opposite numbers from the other hospital. I had no delusions as to the difficulties in the way of amalgamation, for apart from any question of rivalry, the normal desire of any such institution is to maintain its identity and to continue to uphold a tradition of which all the best officers, lay as well as medical, are justly proud. To many, even the idea of a move to a new building is intensely repugnant, for to no small extent tradition becomes associated with one particular group of bricks and mortar. That we should even dream of abandoning the building in Bath Row, and still more that our scheme would mean that in time the "New General" Hospital, barely twenty-five years old, should cease to be a medical school hospital, was to some of our colleagues little short of blasphemy. Nevertheless, I for one, could not see the University sending its medical students to the more distant General when it had at its door a clinical hospital more up-to-date and fully staffed. My own feeling was that bit by bit, the General would be used for other types of hospital cases, such as out-patients, maternity, or accidents. Although with its deficient ancillary services it could not remain a first-class general hospital, it would serve very well indeed for many kinds of special hospital, where so wide a variety of ancillary services would be unnecessary. Naturally these ideas were not formulated in the Grant Robertson Report, but I believe they were in the minds of several of the members of the Committee whilst we were discussing our recommendations. I again stress that we had been asked by the Hospitals' Council to advise on an ideal scheme, but we naturally did not live in the clouds when trying to estimate what would be the ultimate results of our recommendations, if, as most of my colleagues thought unlikely, they were ever carried out.

It was clear that if no amalgamation took place, there was bound to be difficulty in the medical staffing. The position of a clinical teacher at a teaching hospital is one which is most jealously guarded, for the reputation of the consultant largely depends on his teaching status. To me, with my long association with both the General and the Queen's, it would have been quite impossible to agree to any scheme that would not safeguard the position in the medical school of every member of both medical staffs, and if, as I feared, it became necessary to abandon as a general hospital, and as part of the bed-complement used for clinical teaching, either of the two existing hospitals, some at least of our colleagues might be left stranded unless the amalgamation took place, so that transfer from one building to another would be automatic. It is easy now, after the amalgamation has taken place, to regard those cogitations as being of little moment, but to the staff of 1926, and to our junior colleagues in particular, it was a matter of vital importance that their position in the medical school should be assured.

It is a pity that we never managed to find a better name for the amalgamated institution; the name "United Hospital" by which it was later officially known is hardly to be regarded as either euphonious or attractive, but it has the merit of indicating how the hospitals involved came together, though Sands Cox and Alfred Baker, and even Jordan Lloyd and Thomas Chevasse, might well have considered that the world was coming to an end before such a monstrous act of union should be even conceived.

I have said nothing here of the attitude of the others who would be affected by amalgamation. No-one likes to have curtailed the freedom that he has hitherto enjoyed, and there is always some irksome restraint to be met when two bodies are brought together. The medical men were more likely to be acquiescent than the laymen, especially those who had been on the committees for many years. The nursing staff would be for the time all upset, and the administrative staff were likely to look askance at any such move, lest their positions be jeopardised. It would take a generation to rebuild in unified form the traditions which had become the guiding lights of the two hospitals, whose combined ages amounted to nearly 250 years.

If, at this point, I may jump forward some years to analyse the reactions of the Board of the General and the Committee of Management of the Queen's, it became more and more obvious as time went on, that both hospitals looked askance at amalgamation. Neither Board believed in 1926 that the scheme for building a third hospital at Edgbaston was feasible, and as the difficulties of maintaining the General and the Queen's increased, the more conservative members of both became more and more adamant in their determination to maintain their independence. It was only after six years of persistent pressure, and after the first bricks had been laid at Metchley, when it became certain that their particular institution might suffer partial eclipse if they remained aloof, that they were prepared to take the steps necessary for amalgamation. Without any display of enthusiasm, both hospitals then agreed to promote a Bill in Parliament to amalgamate the two for all purposes.

I will not weary the reader with the details which had to be agreed; suffice it to say that the laws, bye-laws and regulations of both hospitals had to be examined, and where, as they often did, they differed, a compromise had to be found that would be acceptable to both. This work was spread over many months and the two institutions are greatly indebted to Mr. Edmund Beale of the General and Mr. John Glaisyer of the Queen's for the care they bestowed on this rather dreary work.

The amalgamation became effective in 1933, Sir Charles Hyde being elected the first President of the "United Hospital".

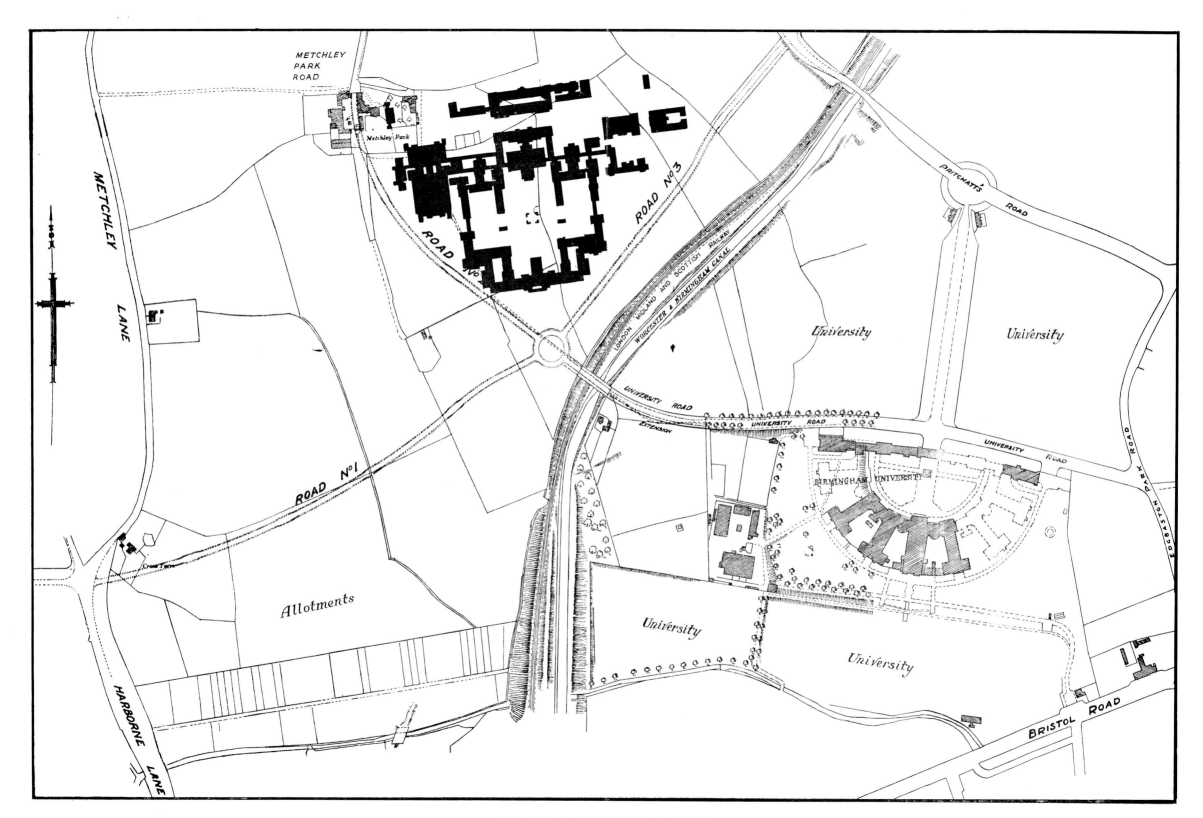

THE SITE OF THE HOSPITALS CENTRE
(1930)

CHAPTER XII

THE SITE OF THE HOSPITALS CENTRE

THE land so generously bought and presented to the city by Messrs. Cadbury Brothers, consisted of a compact, and apart from the section reserved for allotments, nearly square area, occupying 100 acres. At the time of purchase in October, 1926, there were few buildings there; a farm house, and a few barns and other agricultural buildings of no great value dotted the northern section, and the remains of the "Metchley Lodge" mentioned elsewhere was outlined to the north-west. The site lies about two miles from the centre of the city of Birmingham, where the three suburbs of Edgbaston, Selly Oak and Harborne adjoin: it is separated from the land belonging to the University, and on which the Science Faculty had already been built, by the Midland Railway line to Bristol, and the Worcester Canal which here runs near to and parallel with the railway. The land slopes away rather sharply to the south and west, and both railway and canal are hidden from view to the north, as they run mainly in a cutting.

The lower section of the site, about fifty acres in area, is not suitable for building, and in the conveyance to the city, this land was expressly reserved for allotments; the rest of the land, at an average height of some 470 feet above sea level, is reserved for hospital buildings. Certain conditions were laid down in the covenant which affected our plans. It was expressly stated that any chimney-stack must be built south of a certain line drawn on the plans, in order to preserve the amenities of the residential suburbs. It was also agreed that no cases of insanity or infectious fevers should be treated there, and a further clause barred the city from using any part of the site for the building of houses, other than those needed for the housing of hospital employees or nurses.

Although certain of the more northerly sections of the site were to be used as playing fields until they were required for hospital building, it was clear that the area reserved for hospital work would be sufficient to house three thousand patients, with normal forms of construction. We could therefore hope that at long last, an area was now reserved for hospital development which would meet the needs of Birmingham for at least half a century. (See also Appendix, page 139).

This munificent gift of land, in exactly the right place to meet the wishes of the University and the medical staffs concerned with the teaching of students, inaugurated a welcome change in the attitude of the committees of the General and Queen's Hospitals; in a single day, it swept away the suspicions that the Hospitals Council had been merely used as a cloak to cover the design of transferring the two teaching hospitals to civic control. The speedy way in which after the halting of the extension schemes of the two hospitals, the gift had been made, showed the alternative of building at Metchley was not a dream but a possible reality; although at this stage, in 1926, and indeed up to the first of January, 1933, many members of both hospital boards still doubted the feasibility of the construction on financial grounds. It was for this reason more than any other that neither board of management was prepared to accept that amalgamation which had been one of the cardinal points in the Grant Robertson Report.

———

CHAPTER XIII

INTERIM

THE collapse of the General Hospital Extension Scheme, and the completion of the meetings of the Grant Robertson Committee left me free once more to devote my time to my life's work, the treatment of patients in private and at the General Hospital, and the teaching of students. I was now no longer either chairman or deputy-chairman of the Medical Committee, and after some six years spent in somewhat intensive committee work, I felt that some other of my fellow members might well take on the task of getting for our hospital what was necessary to prevent our sliding downhill.

Like most of our colleagues, both medical and lay, I had little hope that the advice we had given in the Grant Robertson Report would be translated into bricks and mortar. Even after the first step had been taken, and the land had been provided in the right place and in generous acreage, the obstacles to be surmounted were formidable. One of the worst was the uniting of the General and Queen's Hospitals, for in addition to the normal resistance of such bodies to losing one iota of their freedom and identity, there was a century of dissension to be liquidated. Added to this, we, as a voluntary hospital knew how difficult was the collection of funds, and we had little hope that in this matter we should have the continued goodwill of those who controlled the other hospitals. The task of collecting from voluntary sources something like a million pounds from our city, with so many other charitable organisations expecting help from the same pool, meant that their present passive neutrality might at any moment be translated into active opposition. As our previous experience had shown, it was finance that was most likely to make the scheme impossible.

During this fallow period, when nothing tangible seemed to be happening, some of the special hospitals approached the Hospitals Council, in order to find out whether they might also build on the Metchley site. Like the two general hospitals, they were suffering from overcrowding, deficiency of beds and out-patient accommodation; all the Council could do was to promise them that their turn would come later, and they must wait till the general hospital was built; at the same time, they were not to make any public appeal, lest it cut across the appeal on behalf of the Centre.

At their meeting on June 28th, 1927, the Medical Committee of the General Hospital were asked to appoint two representatives to become members of what afterwards was called the Executive Board of the Hospitals Centre. Normally, one of the representatives would be the chairman of the committee, but Mr. Beckwith

Whitehouse declined to serve, and, in my absence on holiday, they appointed me as one of the two. On my return, I protested that I had done, fruitlessly, a vast amount of committee work in the previous six years, and begged to be excused. It was, however, pointed out that the senior surgeon, Professor Leonard Gamgee had accepted as one nominee, and as I was now the senior physician, I ought to accept the other representative position; it was added that my previous experience might be an asset. I discussed the position with many of my colleagues and personal friends, for I had no delusions as to what this might mean. Under pressure from all sides, I agreed to serve, on condition that my views coincided with those of the medical staff, and that they would back me up if, as I expected, our wishes clashed with those of others on the new Board.

I therefore asked them to agree to the following propositions:

(1) We would only co-operate in the building of the new hospital on condition that the University Medical School should be built on adjacent land.

(2) This must be a large hospital, capable of becoming ultimately *the* medical school hospital of the University.

(3) When complete, the hospital should be managed by the combined General and Queen's Hospitals, and should not be a third and independent hospital.

They were in cordial agreement with these principles, and I found that the medical staff were substantially unanimous. We also discussed the possibility of the establishment of whole-time Chairs in Medicine, Surgery and Gynaecology, but as this was an academic problem at that stage, there being no funds available or in sight wherewith to set up such professorships, no actual resolution was taken; all that was indicated by some of the members was that if such chairs were established, they should not be located, as far as clinical work was concerned, away from their other clinical colleagues, for much of their inspiration would then be lost.

At the end of the meeting, after I had accepted nomination, I reminded the members that they had given me no support when our own Extension Scheme was *in extremis*, and that if I were to find that for some reason or other they again changed their minds, I might be expected to take my own line whatever they said. I also reminded them that it might well be impossible to build both hospital and school at the same time, and they must take the risk of the University changing its avowed intention of rebuilding the Medical School at Edgbaston. The risk involved in such a change of plan, over which we had no control, was also accepted by the staff.

It was thus clear to me that the medical staff of the General Hospital fully concurred in the findings and recommendations of the Grant Robertson Report, and it was on that basis that I accepted nomination as one of their representatives on the Centre Board.

CHAPTER XIV

THE WORK OF THE EXECUTIVE BOARD

NEARLY two years elapsed between the halting of the schemes for extending the General and Queen's Hospitals, and the first meeting of the Executive Board of the Centre. During this period, two measures of importance were initiated by Alderman Cadbury. The first was the purchase and the conveyance to the city of the site of the proposed hospital centre, announced on October 19th, 1926; a note on this site appears on page 61. The second was that a series of deputations was arranged to visit hospitals of repute on the continent and in America. These visits were made by various members of the staffs of the General and Queen's Hospitals, together with Alderman and Mrs. W. A. Cadbury, and on their return the results of their visits were put together and the conclusions printed in book form; the whole of the expenses and of visits and printing were defrayed by Alderman Cadbury. The cities visited included Rome, Genoa, Naples, Lyons, Paris, Hamburg, Copenhagen, Leipzig, Berlin and Helsingborg (Sweden). Mr. A. H. Leaney went alone to America, and a somewhat longer report of conditions and recommendations was printed as a separate report. We also had the advantage of hearing from others of our staffs who sent in observations and suggestions from other cities in the British Isles, and in Australia.

The Executive Board of the Centre was set up as a result of a resolution passed by the Hospitals Council in September, 1927, and the first meeting took place on October 13th, 1927, with Alderman Cadbury in the chair. The first Board consisted of:

The Lord Mayor of Birmingham (Alderman A. H. James),
The Chairman of the Hospitals Council (Alderman W. A. Cadbury),
  both of whom were *ex-officio* members.
Four members from each of the General and Queen's Hospitals, of whom two
  were medical and two administrative:

The General—	The Queen's—
Dr. Stanley Barnes	Professor W. Billington
Mr. Frank Barnes	Dr. J. G. Emanuel
Mr. E. P. Beale	Mr. W. E. Adlard
Mr. Owen Thompson	Mr. H. F. Keep

One member nominated by the City Council, Councillor Harold Roberts.
One nominated by the University, Principal Sir Charles Grant Robertson.
One nominated by the Chamber of Commerce, Mr. C. E. Greener.

Three by the Hospital Saturday Fund: Mr. W. S. Aston, Mr. T. H. Prust, Mr. C. E. Stephens.

One by the other branches of the Contributory Scheme, Mr. Bertram Ford.

The first resolution agreed was to the effect that the Executive Board should have charge of the first section of the Scheme, namely, the provision of beds of a general character. The second appointed the Principal of the University to act as Chairman.

One of the first subjects to be discussed was the making of roads to and through the site, and the City Surveyor indicated that we could not proceed without the sanction of both the Ministry of Health and the Ministry of Transport.

A further resolution requested the two legal members of the Board, Mr. E. P. Beale and Councillor Harold Roberts, to advise on the best method of conferring on the Board the powers necessary to carry out their functions as delegated by the Hospitals Council.

At the second meeting of the Board on November 10th, there was received the report of the medical and laymen who had visited other hospitals, at home and abroad; this report is reprinted as an Appendix on page 135. The report indicated cogent reasons why the pavilion system of layout was less desirable for our purpose than the corridor system, with three or more storeys to each block. A second departure from the usual English system, was the provision on a wide scale of rooms accessory to the wards. A tour of some American hospitals was made by Mr. A. H. Leaney, and a somewhat more detailed report was later received; and a verbal one by Professor W. Billington, on arrangements made at Glasgow, was also considered by the committee of the Board set up to make recommendations.

In these early days, Mr. (afterwards Sir Frank) Wiltshire acted as honorary secretary, but as the work increased it became necessary to appoint a whole-time officer for secretarial duties, and in December, 1928, Captain J. E. Stone, F.S.A.A., was appointed. For many months he was our only stipendiary officer, and even when it was decided that we would not appoint an appeals officer, he was able with the assistance of the late Mrs. Buttery, to combine this work with the secretarial work.

It was a disappointment to those of us who had been working at the Extension Schemes of the General and Queen's Hospitals, that there was so long a delay in launching the appeal for the building fund. It was to be nearly three years after the Executive Board was set up before the appeal was ultimately made in the Town Hall. Our anxiety, and I speak here more particularly for the medical members of the Board, was due to a close appreciation of the position at our own hospitals, and the difficulties they were encountering in carrying on their work. Moreover, we knew by now that finance was likely to be the worst bugbear in carrying through the building scheme, and many of our friends on the Board of the General and on the Committee of the Queen's were strongly of opinion that we should never get the money necessary. At the same time, we technical officers were asked to work out a schedule of our requirements, in order that a close estimate might be made of the cost; we should have worked much more enthusiastically if we had had a feeling all the time that we were not again being asked to plough the sands.

Looking back over those days, I am not sure that we could have progressed much more quickly. The advice which had been given by various national and municipal officers connected with hospital costs, all tended to indicate that we ought to get through at a cost of some six or seven hundred pounds a bed, for all of these advisers had been more accustomed to dealing with chronic hospitals and infirmaries, in which not only is the nursing staff more exiguous than in a medical school hospital, but there is no necessity to provide for a large number of out-patients and ancillary services. Naturally we had to satisfy the business men on the Board that the provisions we were requiring were necessary, and those of us who had had some experience could only think in terms of a thousand pounds a bed; in fact, if we were to be asked to create—or help in designing—yet another hospital on exactly the same lines as the other hospitals in the city, we were no longer prepared to co-operate.

In the long run, we managed to convince those who dominated the financial position on our Board, that all the extras that we wanted were desirable, and that they were not just medical fads.

A serious cause of delay was the difficulty of establishing our legal position with the Board of Trade, and of getting them to agree the clause we wanted to insert whereby we might hand over the hospital when complete to the combined General and Queen's Hospitals. The Board's position was that these two hospitals were not united, and they were not prepared to give us power to dispose of a million pounds' worth of property, created from public funds, to a hypothetical body. The exclusion of this clause was likely, as we well knew, to cause suspicion in the two existing hospitals that we were intending to build a third and independent one; eventually a compromise was found that enabled us to allow the management, but not the ownership, to be given to some other body.

As at this time we had in view the coming of the other voluntary hospitals to the site, and as their position would be to a considerable degree affected both by the type and the cost of the buildings we erected, we varied the constitution of the Board by including representatives of each of the special hospitals which, as far as we could foresee, would be likely to move to the Centre Site when they had the opportunity of rebuilding. At the same time, we changed our title from Hospital Centre to Hospitals Centre. Our Memorandum and Articles of Association were altered accordingly, and were at long last approved by the Board of Trade.

ROADS

Further delay was caused by difficulties which arose with the Ministry of Transport. It appeared that the Ministry had already in view the building of an arterial road through the site, in order to by-pass the centre of the city of Birmingham between the city of Coventry and Wolverhampton. This road would cut through the site from north-west to south-east, and was intended to carry heavy traffic; it would cross the canal and railway bridge and continue along University Road. Such a road with its heavy traffic would of course make work at the University with delicate instruments impossible; and it would be equally objectionable to the hospital we were contemplating, for there would be no peace, day or night, for patients or nurses. It was only after a long argument, and when the University made it clear that such a course would mean the rebuilding of the University elsewhere, that the Ministry gave way.

It was, of course, necessary that there should be access to the site for cars, ambulances, buses, and such small numbers of lorries as would be needed for Hospital and University purposes, but we were agreed that all extraneous traffic should be kept out of the Centre if it appeared likely to cause any hardship to patients or resident staffs, or any difficulty in maintaining the scientific services of the Hospital or Medical School. For these reasons, it was essential that the body which managed the Centre, when the hospitals had been completed should have such control over the traffic through the site that all heavy vehicles could be prevented from traversing the area; and eventually the roads that were built for car traffic and that of the University were "private" in the sense that full control was vested in the University and the Centre. In order to make the position clear without the necessity of setting up control gateways, signs were set up at the four entrances to the site, and all roads were constructed on a narrow basis, the usual width being eighteen feet. We were happy in receiving as a gift towards our expenses the making of the roads by the City Council through the site, for otherwise the cost of our work would have been increased by some £20,000.

At a later stage, the City also contributed to our well-being by establishing the No. 2B bus service, which gives direct access to the site for patients' friends and workers at the Medical School.

I do not propose here to follow in detail the minutes of either the Board or the Building Committee. It will be understood that while these negotiations were being carried on, a schedule of our requirements was worked out by a sub-committee, consisting largely of the medical members representing the General and the Queen's Hospitals, together with the secretary, Captain Stone. At the same time, steps were taken to appoint an Architect assessor, a position which was accepted by Mr. Percy Adams.

———————

CHAPTER XV

THE APPEAL AND SCHEDULE

The Appeal for public subscription to provide funds to build the new general hospital on the Metchley site was eventually launched in the Town Hall on April 11th, 1930. The Chair was taken by the Lord Mayor (Alderman M. L. Lancaster), and the speakers included the Minister of Health (Mr. Arthur Greenwood), Mr. Neville Chamberlain, and Mr. L. S. Amery. All speakers proclaimed that this was a far-sighted scheme, and heartily commended it to the citizens of Birmingham.

The response to the Appeal was immediate, for of course there had already been much spade work done. By June 6th, 1930, cash and firm promises had reached a total of £478,000 and now for the first time many of us were beginning to believe that the building would actually take place. By December of the same year the figure had reached £584,000, and by December of 1931 the gifts and promises under covenant had reached £625,000, for even with progressively slackening trade conditions, making the collection of voluntary subscriptions so difficult, the personal generosity and boundless energy of Mr. Harry Vincent had added £40,000 to the fund in a single year.

Although the Appeal for funds was not formally launched for nearly three years after the Executive Board was set up, it need hardly be said that much preliminary work had been done. Not only had the medical members, with the assistance of the secretary, completed a schedule of the items that they considered to be necessary for a modern hospital such as we were contemplating, but an architect had been appointed as a result of a competition. The latter was based on the schedule, set out in the necessary form by the assessor architect, Mr. Percy Adams. In all, ten architects or firms of architects were asked to send in drawings for the competition, and four prizes were offered. All the drawings were assembled in the Art Gallery for members of the Board and of the public to inspect, and they were adjudged by the assessor in the following order:

First   ..   Messrs. Lanchester and Lodge.

Second ..   Mr. S. N. Cooke.

Third   ..   Mr. C. E. Elcock.

Fourth ..   Jointly by Messrs. Pete, Son, and Fairweather, and Messrs. W. and T. Milburn.

For the purpose of the competition the Medical School was included in the design, although the Executive Board was only indirectly concerned with this building; the Medical School constituted the home of the Faculty of Medicine, and was constructed by the same architects at the charge of the University.

Although rough estimates had already been prepared, it had not, up to this stage, been possible to obtain estimates on the architects' drawings; and it was only now that a close approximation to the costs could be obtained. It was upon these estimates that the Appeal was made, and the estimates were, of course, based on prices of labour and materials prevailing in 1930.

The schedule as sent out to the competing architects is a bulky document, and it is not possible to reproduce it here; an abstract would probably be misleading, and I therefore give only the costs of various sections of the work (see Appendix, page 133). By the time at which we were permitted by the Lord Mayor's Conference to commence building in 1933, costs had so far risen that the amount of money, in hand and in sight, would be insufficient to cover the whole of the building as planned, and many items were cut out as a temporary measure. These exclusions comprised the whole of the west wing, representing some 180 beds; all the out-patient and casualty blocks; the night nurses' wing and the maids' quarters, the chapel and the refectory for the visiting staffs, and the rooms designed for clinical teaching in the departments of medicine, surgery and gynaecology.

CHAPTER XVI

THE GATHERING STORM

MANY of us consider that we could devise more efficient conditions and ways of working for those in other trades or professions; few welcome any change imposed from without upon our own. To those who have been employed for many years in one particular building, the prospect of changing over to another is regarded with a critical eye. Still more is it difficult to get anyone who has worked happily in a great hospital for many years to agree that a change so great as the transfer of all authority to a new body not yet in being, and of much activity to a new hospital miles away, is desirable. All of us, medical and laymen alike, who had served the General and Queen's, were proud of our position in a great charity which had been acclaimed in Birmingham for a century or more.

When the Extension Scheme for the General Hospital was turned down by the Hospitals Council, a body which contained only three representatives of the General, I believe it is true to say that without exception those responsible for the management of the hospital were of opinion that a mistake had been made. True, those whose duty it would have been to collect the £250,000 necessary were relieved that someone else could now be left to make whatever financial arrangements were required, and that a few of our younger medical colleagues with less experience of the difficulties and delays that were likely, were not perturbed by the change of plans. Most of us on the senior staff were anxious lest the delay in bringing the hospital up-to-date would seriously undermine its efficiency, result in a loss of prestige, and prevent its giving to the city the same high professional standard of service that had become traditional.

Elsewhere I have described what happened in the interval between the "halting" of the General Hospital Extension Scheme and the setting up of the Executive Board in 1927; my colleague as a representative of the General on the Board was Mr. L. P. Gamgee, but as he was due to leave the active staff of the hospital in a few months, he was only involved in the earlier discussions. His successor, Mr. Frank Barnes, also remained for only a few months, when he was succeeded by Mr. Seymour Barling. Our opposite numbers from the Queen's were Mr. William Billington, whose untimely death early in 1932 was a great blow to his many friends and to the Centre; and Dr. J. G. Emanuel, who was to remain with us throughout the whole of the active period of the Executive Board, and who is still, I am happy to say, serving with us. It was unfortunate in many ways that the surgeons could not maintain continuity of service over the formative years, for during the six years that elapsed after the halting of the Extension Schemes, and before we were ready to start building, all sorts of difficulties were arising at the hospitals.

It was one of the troubles that occurred as a result of the long period of incubation of the Centre Scheme that the Committees of Management and the medical committees were tending to become dichotomised. None of the laymen or the medical representatives of the two hospitals was on the retired list, and to all of them the work involved in preparation of plans at the Centre was something to be added to a normally full programme of work. The result was that for many of the medical and some of the laymen, a decision had to be taken as to whether they should attend the meetings at the Centre or those at the General and Queen's Hospitals. Gradually, it became obvious to those on the Centre Committee that their work there could not be shelved, and they were compelled to cut down their attendances at the Boards of Management of their hospitals, and the corresponding medical committees. Thus in each hospital there arose a division of responsibility as between those who were mainly working to maintain the existing hospitals, and those who were more directly concerned over plans for the new buildings on the Centre site. Little by little, the cleavage between the two groups grew, and as the difficulty of keeping the hospitals working became accentuated, owing to the worsening of the financial situation in 1931, every problem which came up for discussion at the hospitals appeared to be incapable of solution, at least to one group, because so much money was being diverted to the building of the Centre hospital.

Had the General Hospital been free so to do, their normal way of relieving the financial trouble they were experiencing would have been to make a public appeal, for long experience of the generosity of the public made it certain that a sufficient sum would be subscribed to enable them to weather the storm; but the ban on any such appeal by the Hospitals Council still remained, and the mounting deficits and overdraft of the hospital formed a glaring contrast to the six hundred thousand pounds in gifts and firm promises already at the disposal of the Centre.

To the Queen's Hospital, the long delay, together with the ban on any public appeal, caused difficulty in maintenance, but not quite of the same nature as at the rival hospital. When the order came from the Hospitals Council to arrest their Extension Scheme, the ward blocks were already up to the first storey, and it was obvious that this section of the building programme must be completed. The provision of the auxiliary and ancillary services was held up, and as a result the modernisation that had been projected was in abeyance; thus the balance between beds and services was upset, and as their chairman of committee said at a later stage, "It would appear that the Queen's Hospital is condemned to a lingering death". At the same meeting in 1927, the president, Sir Charles Hyde, observed what a pity it was that the decision of the Hospitals Council was timed in 1926, instead of three years earlier when the extensions to the hospital were being planned. In fact, the new wards were opened before the end of the year 1927, so that, apart from finance, it was possible to carry on the work of the Queen's without undue strain while they were waiting for the new beds to become available at Edgbaston.

To these financial and administrative troubles must be added yet another cause for dissension. It will be remembered that the Board of Trade had insisted that we, the Centre, might not have power to hand over the Centre Hospital, when complete, to the united General and Queen's Hospitals. Although the position was explained to the two Boards, many members were convinced that this was a mere quibble, and that the real reason was that it was the intention of those who were building the Centre, to administer it when complete as a separate or third general hospital in the city. They knew, of course, that such action would result in the two older hospitals being ultimately squeezed out of the Medical School, with the great loss in prestige which such a step would entail.

It so happened at this period that I was unable to attend as frequently as I wished at the committees of the General Hospital. In the spring of 1931, I had accepted the position of Dean of the Medical School, largely with the intention of furthering the Centre Scheme, and helping the University to build the Medical School at Edgbaston. This year, also, I was President of the Section of Neurology of the Royal Society of Medicine in London, and it became my duty to attend many meetings at Wimpole Street. In the result, my attendance at board and committee meetings of the General Hospital was very much restricted, and for a time ceased completely when in the autumn of 1931 I was struck down by a serious illness, and unable for some six or seven weeks to take any part in the work of the hospitals, the Centre or the University.

By the time, at very long last, that we were ready in 1931 to start building at the Centre, the country was passing through the greatest financial crisis in her history since the "Hungry Forties" of a hundred years before. To a manufacturing city like ours, this meant crisis on a colossal scale. Works and factories were being closed down for lack of orders, prices of goods were falling, and the figures of unemployment reached appalling heights. As always, in times of financial stringency, the voluntary hospitals were hardest hit, for the gifts from charitable sources as well as the contributions from potential patients were falling to levels which did not allow of proper maintenance of the hospital services.

As I slowly recovered from my illness, and during my stay in the nursing home in November, 1931, I had ample opportunity to consider how we might bring into use the new hospital when it was constructed. It was obvious that the sudden addition of some 750 beds to the complement of the "acute" beds, would involve so many additions to the staffs, especially the medical and nursing staffs, that thereafter some of them might become redundant. Further, now that there was general acceptance of the idea of a large hospital, might we not, to some extent, placate the opposition of those who were afraid of so large an institution being built, if we modified the bed complement in the first instance? It would, of course, be necessary to build up a large number of departments—like the X-rays—to the

750-bed level in the first instance, and this course would mean that the average cost per bed would be greatly increased. Such a course would still enable the "ideal" hospital to be completed in later days, for the ancillary services for the full quota of beds would be available.

I came to the conclusion that the best way to solve this problem, was to build in the first instance only five hundred of the beds, making sure that the architect could so arrange the construction that wherever the service was inexpansible, it should be built up to the full scale of 750 in the first instance. I recognised that this would mean that the average cost per bed would be very high, and that the honorary treasurer might not welcome the change of plans, but from a very general survey, this seemed to be the best solution of the difficulty, and was one which might make its appeal to those who said that already there were nearly enough beds in the city.

When Sir Charles Grant Robertson and Mr. Vincent came to see me in the nursing home, we made of the occasion a sub-committee meeting, and after a long discussion, and a few days to think it over, came to the conclusion that this was the best way in which we could meet the situation that had arisen.

On November 26th, 1931, I was able once more to attend the meeting of the Executive Board, and two important resolutions were on the agenda. The first, Resolution "A" was as follows:

"The Board reaffirms its agreement with the policy and programme laid down in the Birmingham Hospitals Centre Scheme, and for the carrying out of which it was incorporated, and issued with the approval of the General and Queen's Hospitals its appeal, and decides that it proposes to give immediate effect to this policy by bringing into existence at the earliest possible date, as a first instalment of the whole scheme, a Hospital Unit of five hundred beds, with the necessary nursing block, auxilliary services and administration block, together with the re-organised Medical School of the University, which is a necessary and integral part of the Scheme. The Board leaves to future consideration the date and method of carrying out further and successive instalments of the scheme, until the whole as planned and previously accepted, has at the appropriate date been completed".

This resolution was passed by a vote of twenty-two to two, the only dissentients being the chairman and house governor of the Queen's Hospital.

A second Resolution "B" was then discussed. This stated that:

"The Board appoints a Committee to confer with the lay and medical representatives of the General and Queen's Hospitals, together with the Chairman of the Hospitals Council, to consider and report to this Board, to the Boards of the two hospitals concerned and to the Council and Medical Faculty of the University on (a) the present position and relations of the two hospitals to the Hospitals Centre, and to the University as defined in Resolution "A", (b) their position during the period in which the first instalment of the Hospitals Centre will be completed;

and (c), their position and relations to the Centre Scheme as a whole, after the first instalment has been brought into effective existence".

This resolution was also accepted, and to be our representatives there were appointed, the chairman, the honorary treasurer, the chairman of the appeal committee (Alderman M. L. Lancaster), Alderman Cadbury, Mr. Smedley Aston, and myself. In fact, this committee was never completed; the work it was intended to accomplish was carried out by what was afterwards called the "Lord Mayor's Conference", appointed some two months later.

The passing of the Resolution "A" appeared to act as a percussion cap in touching off the explosive material that has been accumulating for so long. Up to that time, the two general hospitals had not believed that the building of the Centre Hospital was a project of more than academic interest; many members of the two boards of management still did not believe that the scheme was likely to be carried out. At the same time, the fact that subscriptions and firm promises had been accumulated until they reached already six hundred thousand pounds, excited the imagination of those who saw their own hospitals languishing for lack of funds. What could not they, the existing hospitals, accomplish if only this enormous sum could be diverted into the right channel!

CHAPTER XVII

CONTROVERSY

THE first shot in the controversy was fired by "A Birmingham Medical Man", in the form of a letter to the *Birmingham Post*, in the issue of November 17th, 1931. The letter began, "As it is proposed to begin building operations on the new site at Edgbaston in the near future, the present moment seems opportune to review the position of the hospital position question in Birmingham". After giving a précis of the position up to the time of the Grant Robertson Report, and looking at the problem from the Medical School point of view as well as that of the Hospitals Council, he put forward two main arguments for postponing building. In the first place, between the time of the issue of the Grant Robertson Report and the year 1930, "there have been provided in Birmingham and district 500 beds in Voluntary and 379 in Public Assistance hospitals....it seems obvious that the provision of a large number of additional beds in Birmingham is no longer required". The second point made was that the maintenance of the hospital would require about £150,000 a year, "and with the finances of the old hospitals in the state they are in, how is another hospital of even 350 beds to be maintained?" Most of the rest of the letter gave reasons why a hospital of 300 beds would be a further handicap rather than an asset to the Medical School.

This letter was not answered by any member of the Executive Board immediately; Sir Charles, Mr. Vincent and I had a short meeting that morning, and decided that it would be better to wait and see what happened. Three days later, the second letter was published from "Another Medical Man". In the main, this letter underlined the points made in the previous one, more particularly as to costs both of construction and subsequent maintenance. He asked, is this hospital a necessity or a luxury? He went on to argue that as about a thousand beds had been added to the complement of Birmingham and district since the days when, in 1926, the deficiency was fixed at 600 to 800, the leeway had been completely made up, and that already there were some redundant beds. "I know for a fact that many are unoccupied at the present moment". He then went on to discuss the value of such a hospital to the Medical School, and said that the two existing hospitals already provided 821 beds for clinical teaching, a higher percentage than in many other medical schools. He put forward the possibility that "the bankrupt hospital may have to be turned over to the municipality—a thing that many seem to dread". "The Birmingham Medical School has every reason to be proud of its past and its present; but it will never be a large school".

It will be noted that both of these letters were unsigned, but it was obvious to members of the Board that the writers had an extensive inside knowledge of the Medical School and the two teaching hospitals. Messages from the *Birmingham Daily Post* were received by us indirectly, assuring us that they were written by important men whose opinions would carry weight in the city. I suppose that none of us likes to be criticised, and the reaction to a criticism which is made anonymously must usually be "if they believe this, why not put their names to the letters?" Several other letters appeared in the *Post* during the next few days, and on the 26th of November there appeared a leading article stressing the points already put forward in the anonymous letters.

After the leader in the *Post*, it was no longer possible to refrain from reply, if only because of the prominent position occupied by the proprietor, Sir Charles Hyde, in our hospital world. It was therefore agreed between us that Sir Charles Grant Robertson as chairman should issue on our behalf a full statement of the position, and a short history of how the scheme came into being. This was published in the *Post* on December 3rd, and was a fighting reply to our critics. "The Executive Board is not a self-appointed body of enthusiastic amateurs, unversed in hospital requirements and medical practice or in business generally.... It is not unfair to suggest that this body of workers has been wrestling with all the problems concerned, and that it has never at any time rushed blindly into important or unimportant decisions.... The public will draw a false inference if they suppose, or are led to suppose for one moment, that the Executive Board of the Centre, with five years' continuous study and work behind it, has not appreciated the tremendous responsibility of the trust which has been committed to it".

On the 4th December a letter appeared in the *Post* which gave the views of those of us medical men who had been actively promoting the scheme; it was a two-column letter, and was signed by physicians and surgeons at the General, the Queen's and the Children's Hospitals. In this letter we pointed out that there were three main elements, the scheme in general, the finance, and the deficiency in beds. Although our medical critics had made much of the financial question, we refused to be drawn into a discussion on that point, as it was not one "upon which medical men can speak with authority". Many of the arguments which have already been put forward in an earlier chapter on the question of the numbers of beds necessary, were re-iterated in this letter, including our reaction to the two most usual methods employed to combat a deficiency by setting up extra beds and by turning out patients prematurely. We added, "We cannot stress too much that in all our discussions about accommodation we have always put the interests of the patients first, and that if we are compelled to continue under the conditions as they exist today, we are not giving that service to our patients to which they are entitled".

A reply to this manifesto came on December 7th, this time in the form of a signed letter from Professor L. P. Gamgee; it was now generally believed that the original letter "from a local medical man" was sent by him, and that the "Another

Medical Man" was Dr. Douglas Stanley. In this letter Mr. Gamgee criticised his colleagues for not discussing the financial aspect of the scheme "I know the writers too well to think that they are without experience of finance". He then went on to combat the assertion that beds were still short, and put forward the suggestion that the stay of patients in the General and Queen's Hospitals might be still further shortened, if they could be moved out at an earlier stage to a convalescent hospital some ten of fifteen miles out in the country; and that the two main hospitals should have some money spent on them—a comparatively small amount. The point was again made that to transfer the whole of the clinical material to the south-west of the city, when the industrial area was mainly in the north and east, would "tamper dangerously with this supply".

As was to be expected, there followed a series of letters of less importance from those interested in hospitals, and from business men. Most of the letters were critical of our decision to carry on, and most of them were based on the cost of making the financial provision—either for the building or for the maintenance of the three general hospitals when the new one was in being. On December 8th there appeared a letter signed by Dr. Douglas Stanley, in which he replied to our manifesto of December 4th. Like Mr. Gamgee, he objected to our by-passing of the financial question. "Why can they not own up and say that the new hospital will have to be paid for and maintained?" The other arguments put forward in the letter went over much the same ground that had already been covered, and included some observations on the type of cases admitted and those from which the students were taught.

Most of the other letters to the papers followed the lines of the earlier criticisms, and only a handful were favouring the scheme. This may well have been because the members of the Board thought it desirable to leave to the Chairman the task of replying, and his three letters, each occupying some two columns of the *Birmingham Post*, were almost the only replies to the critics. The letter which determined the Board to consult the subscribers was one written by the Chancellor of the Exchequer, Mr. Neville Chamberlain, on December 12th. It will be remembered that this was the period when, owing to intense depression of world trade, we had, only a few weeks before, "gone off gold", and naturally the Chancellor was dominated by the idea of economy. This, indeed, was the main burden of his argument.... "the need for public economy had laid fresh burdens on the nation and involved all classes in new and searching sacrifices". He ended his letter by advising that the subscribers should be called together for consultation. This letter from one of our earliest and most important supporters, was published in the same edition of the *Post* as a communication from the Medical Officer of Health, in which the point was made that the bed shortage of 1926 had already been met. "This increase.... has come partly through actual provision of beds at voluntary hospitals; to a small extent through the decreasing demands from outside areas; but largely by an increasing effectiveness in the use of existing bed accommodation". In a summary, the Medical Officer of Health said "It would thus appear that the situation in regard to bed accommodation in Birmingham hospitals (voluntary and official) has changed radically since the issue of the joint report in 1926, in directions which it would be impossible for the authors of that report to forecast".

The simultaneous publication of these two communications made it imperative to consult the whole body of our supporters and subscribers; the one said that national responsibilities made retrenchment necessary, the other that the whole *raison d'etre* of our existence had been swept away. Although we could not accept the position as outlined by the Medical Officer of Health as being a true picture of the hospital position, and although we believed the attitude of the Chancellor of the Exchequer to be open to challenge, we clearly understood that we should no longer have the support of the public unless we once more met our opponents, and discussed with them in public the reasons why we still remained of opinion that the scheme should be carried into effect.

It was arranged that a public meeting should be held in the Midland Institute, whose largest hall will accommodate some 600 people. By the time this decision became public property, there was an indication that a very large number of interested people would wish to attend; not only direct subscribers, but many of those who, through various organisations had contributed their quota to the hundreds of thousands of pounds which now constituted the result of our appeal. In addition, there were those who will always be interested in any matter of controversy of a public character, and it was soon apparent that admission must be arranged by a ticket system.

The Midland Institute Meeting, January 4th, 1932

The meeting took place in the Large Hall of the Midland Institute, and the chair was taken by the Lord Mayor, Sir John Burman.

In his introductory remarks the chairman mentioned that he had received letters from some of the larger subscribers, indicating that if the scheme were abandoned, they would not be consenting parties to their subscriptions being diverted to other objects, however worthy they might be. Sir Charles Grant Robertson then read out the solicitor's opinion on the legality of such a diversion of our appeal funds, making it clear that in his opinion, it would be necessary to return all unexpended amounts.

Sir Gilbert Barling then moved:

"That this meeting of subscribers approves the policy of the Executive Board in proceeding forthwith with the first instalment of the Hospitals Centre Scheme". This resolution was seconded by Mr. (later Sir) Harry Vincent, dealing mainly with the finance of the Scheme, and indicating how valuable a contribution immediate building would make to the alleviation of the distress caused by unemployment. Sir Harry made an appeal for immediate building, in order that every advantage could be taken of the low prices prevailing.

Lord Austin moved the following amendment:

"That in view of the grave national financial crisis, and the difficulty of maintaining existing Birmingham voluntary hospitals, this meeting requests the Executive Board of the new Hospitals Centre to postpone building until both the above conditions are more favourable". The amendment was seconded by Mr. T. Oliver Lee, the chairman of the Queen's Hospital. Both speeches made it clear that it was the financial position of the two hospitals, the Queen's and General, which had determined the two chairmen to bring forward this resolution.

Mr. Harold Roberts then spoke on behalf of the original motion, and was followed by Sir Martin Melvin, the chairman of the board of the General Hospital, who favoured postponement on the grounds that the existing hospitals were starved of funds, and that the upkeep of yet another hospital of the size of the one projected would lead to insolvency. The next speaker, Mr. Smedley Aston, spoke on behalf of the Contributory Scheme and the Hospitals Saturday Fund, and advocated an immediate start on the building. He criticised the General Hospital for not having taken advantage of the opportunity to make an appeal for funds since the Hospitals Council had raised their embargo in the previous April. Captain Monk, representing the Dunlop Rubber Company and some 8,000 employees took the line that it would be impossible to maintain the three hospitals by the voluntary system, and that the result would be municipalisation. Captain Stone then spoke in favour of making an immediate start on the building, and argued that certain economies in administration at the existing hospitals would permit of their being financed, together with the existing projected Centre Hospital, with resources already in sight. He was answered by Mr. A. H. Leaney, who was insistent that the cost per bed at the General Hospital was a reasonable one, and that the figures put forward on behalf of those who advocated commencement of building the new hospital at once, were misleading. Dr. Stanley Barnes then spoke in favour of an immediate start, making the point that it was not only a question of beds but of providing the ancillary services so necessary to a modern hospital At the instance of the Lord Mayor, Sir Charles Grant Robertson then wound up the debate on behalf of the Executive Board, and the chairman then put the amendment to the meeting. The result was declared as follows:

| For the Amendment | .. | 214 |
| Against .. | .. | .. | 256 |

| Majority against | .. | 42 |

Thereafter, the Lord Mayor put the original resolution as a substantive resolution, and declared "That is carried by an overwhelming majority". A vote of thanks to the chairman concluded the meeting.

The meeting did but little to further the interests of the Centre. There were too many figures put forward to the audience, and those put forward by one side were often controverted by the other. There was no opportunity for a careful survey of the figures for beds or for costs, and it is probable that the audience as a whole was ill-fitted to deal with the figures presented. Some ill-feeling, too, was introduced by suggestions that the meeting had been "packed", and by various accusations of mismanagement of the existing hospitals. Further, the relatively narrow majority of 42, in a meeting of some 500 people, was too small to ensure the wholehearted support of the city to the furtherance of the scheme.

At the next meeting of the Executive Board, it was decided to invite the Lord Mayor to call a conference of representatives of the General Hospital, the Queen's Hospital, the Hospitals Centre and nominees of the Lord Mayor, to examine the whole problem, including that of finance from the point of view of maintenance when the hospital projected was complete. For the Executive Board, there acted Sir Charles, the chairman; Mr. Harry Vincent, the honorary treasurer; Alderman M. L. Lancaster, the chairman of the appeal committee; Alderman W. A. Cadbury; and Dr. Stanley Barnes, the Dean of the Faculty of Medicine. The independent members appointed by the Lord Mayor were Alderman W. Byng Kenrick, Alderman S. J. Grey, Mr. Peter F. B. Bennett and Mr. F. J. L. Hickinbotham. Their report suggested that the best plan was for the Executive Board to commence building on the first day of January, 1933, and in due course this advice was accepted.

After the report of the Lord Mayor's Conference, the opposition to the Centre gradually died down, and once the preliminary steps had been taken on the site, no overt opposition in the Press distracted us from our task. Naturally there were criticisms, particularly at the slow progress made in the building; there were many of our colleagues who appeared to expect that within two years of the decision to start building, they would be able to move in and start work. It was, in fact, nearly six years from the lifting of the ban that were to elapse before the first patient was admitted.

CHAPTER XVIII

BUILDING

IT is one of the difficulties in planning a hospital that the plan of today is apt to be out-of-date next year, and yet, as it takes at least four years to build a large hospital, it is important that decisions should be made and not varied more than in small matters. Any professional enthusiast is always discovering new ways of improving on his predecessor's plans, and even on those he himself made yesterday. A naval friend of mine goes so far as to declare that in his opinion an aircraft carrier is out-of-date on the day the keel is laid, and many a manufacturer has had trouble with his engineers because they want to change some vital component before he has had a chance to test out what was agreed in the first instance. With a large staff of physicians and surgeons behind us, it was natural that we were constantly being assailed by demands for changes after the main scheme had been agreed, for all these officers had been trained as individualists and all of them were keen on their work.

Where the new or resuscitated idea merely affected a small piece of equipment, no great harm was done, but occasionally a demand was put forward for a fundamental change. A characteristic example was that of the position of the surgical block. In the first instance, it was agreed that this block should be located in the west wing, with the operating theatre block adjacent; but after the plans had been drawn up and the quantities taken out, several of the surgeons wanted a change whereby the east block should serve the surgical section of the hospital, as the operating theatres would then be near the pay block which was expected to be built as soon as the rest of the hospital was complete. Simple as this transfer seemed to the surgeons, it was not so from the point of view of the architect; he could not simply change over the east and west blocks without a major reconstruction of his plans, for the levels were different and the departments of the medical school had to be re-adjusted so that the pathological section should be in apposition to the clinical laboratories. Eventually the change-over was abandoned, the honorary treasurer being shocked at the extra cost which would have been incurred by such a change of plan.

From this stage onwards, those of us who were most intimately concerned with the building programme consulted our medical committees only rarely, and even progress reports were only brought forward to them occasionally.

Once the architect had been appointed, we were in a position to make rapid progress, even if nothing tangible was obvious to our staffs. Decisions had to be

82

taken as to all sorts of finishes, of walls, floors and floorings, and fixtures. At the same time, we needed to decide on all kinds of engineering fixtures, for many of the supply services, including heating and various electric supply conduits, would need to be buried in the walls and floors. The building committee (see page 118), appointed early in 1930 soon after the assessor had made his award to the successful architect, worked with a will, largely under the guidance of Mr. Harry Vincent. Most of the latter half of 1930, and of the early months of 1931, were devoted to work with the architect and engineer, and to arranging the form of the contracts with builders and sub-contractors. For the first time now, it was possible to get fairly accurate figures as to costs, instead of trusting to costs as worked out on a cube basis. In the Appendix on page 133 are given the estimates that were obtained.

I do not propose here to follow the minutes of the building committee; I prefer to take out from them certain items, and give the gist of the reasons why certain decisions were taken. Always we kept in mind that we were to build in accordance with the findings of the Grant Robertson Committee Report as to size and planning for the future. At the same time, our committee was concerned with matters financial, whereas the Grant Robertson Committee made its recommendations on an "ideal" basis. Decisions as to particular items, in the discussions which follow, were always taken on a realistic basis, and although the interests of the prospective patients remained paramount, the cost of various forms of building and equipment often determined the final choice.

Layout of Wards

In consequence of the earlier decisions that the hospital should be of the order of 700 beds, one of the first points to which attention was directed, was as to whether we should build on the pavilion principle, or should accept the multi-storey block as the standard. Our emissaries who went abroad to report on buildings in Europe, America and the Dominions, had seen all types of building; some of these were medical school hospitals, but many were not. We had the opportunity, in the wide space available on the Centre to adopt either plan, and there were many of our advisers and some of our members who favoured the single-storey pavilion plan. Any building so set up could be scrapped in twenty-five years and rebuilt to suit altered circumstances; this method was said by them to have the advantage of being less costly in the first instance, but it was not nearly so much cheaper as appeared at first sight, for the engineering services required would be much more extensive; in addition, the heat losses would be much greater, and for this and other reasons the cost of maintenance was likely to be heavier.

What mainly determined our decision was the difficulty in maintaining cohesion between the various elements of the hospital. We were anxious that at no stage should the various groups of physicians and surgeons get out of touch one with another. The medical members were anxious that the separation of medical services into water-tight compartments, which had been progressing for years as a result of the increasing specialisation, should be arrested if it was possible. Eventually, and after hearing about relative costs from many advisers, we decided that the multi-storey building that would best suit our work, would be one of not more than seven storeys; beyond that figure the cost per bed was increased, owing to the greater amount of steel required in the framework of the building. In fact, the buildings were ultimately designed on the basis that six storeys were above ground, with one basement on the west and two on the east owing to difference in the ground levels.

Needless to say, all wards were to face as nearly due south as possible, so that we might give our patients all possible sunlight. Seeing that the Medical School was to be built on the south aspect of the hospital, it was important that the two should be sufficiently far apart to allow full sunlight and an ample flow of fresh air between them.

The size of the various units under the control of a particular physician or surgeon was an important decision, as it affected the general layout. The intention was that when the honorary physician or surgeon reached the retiring age, he should become a "consulting" officer with a limited number of beds, in which he could continue to treat his patients, but in diminishing numbers. The new "honorary" appointed would then become the official head of the department, with a new assistant who would also have a few beds at once, and as the consultant advanced in years and was responsible for a diminishing number of beds, so the assistant would each year have more beds, the bulk of the unit remaining at the disposal of the honorary officer. Such a system would retain for the hospital the advice and services of an officer of long standing, while relieving him of the obligation of caring for so many patients. At the same time, it was anticipated that when an officer's status changed from honorary to consulting, the former would take over all the committee work and would represent the department on the board of management.

It was assumed that for the service of this group, a registrar would be appointed; he would be a specially selected and trained post-resident, who had accepted the post with the intention of making that particular branch of medicine or surgery his main practice.

For the benefit of those who are not conversant with the terms here used, and which were the ones commonly in practice in the voluntary hospitals, it should be noted that the term "honorary" was always applied to a member of the full staff; the "assistant" was often honorary in that he received little or no pay, and of course the "consulting" officer was unpaid for any work he did in the hospital.

Such a team of workers would serve a considerably larger unit than that common to most voluntary hospitals, but there would be three senior officers as well as three juniors, and it was hoped that if those who managed the hospital would adopt this system, it would permit of the services of an officer no longer young, who could no longer expect to cope with the arduous life of a full physician or surgeon at a voluntary hospital, to retire to consultant standard at a relatively early stage of his career, without losing touch with his hospital work or his colleagues. We felt that this arrangement would be in the best interests of the hospital and the patients, as well as of the medical staff.

Eventually, we decided upon 60 as the number of beds that should constitute a unit, but we were most anxious that they should not be simply in two big wards, one male and one female of thirty each. A long discussion ranged around the question as to how large should be the biggest ward in this unit. Most people when told that they must go into hospital immediately ask whether they can have a separate ward, and in many hospitals for private or paying cases, the wards have been built on that understanding. Experience has shown that a comparatively large proportion of patients prefer to have the company of other patients when they have passed the acute phase of their illness, and the demand for purely medical as opposed to social reasons for single bed rooms, would be satisfied by segregating a relatively small number of beds in this way. So far as cost is concerned, it is of course more expensive to build the patients' dormitory on the single cubicle basis, but the real difficulty comes in the nursing; far larger numbers of nurses are required if the wards are cut up into small units, for supervision of each one is impossible without a large staff.

We compromised. Although single-bedded units might be required, we were building at the moment not a "pay" block—that was to come later—and we decided that the small wards should contain twos and fours, whilst the biggest wards should not contain more than sixteen beds.

The unit of sixty beds was to be designed so that normally thirty of each should be for men and thirty for women. Our experience in hospital work had taught us that often there was a great pressure to admit one sex, when beds allotted for their use were all full, while beds were sometimes vacant in the wards allotted to the other sex. The new set-up would provide the opportunity for the staff to switch over a small ward of two or four beds to the other sex, if the pressure on beds were unequally distributed, so that at any time the numbers might be adjusted to thirty-two, thirty-four or even thirty-six for one sex, with the other proportionately reduced. At the same time, if a patient for any reason needed to be segregated in a single ward, little would be lost by his remaining the sole occupant of a two-bedded one.

Should the beds in a hospital ward be so arranged that the long axis is parallel with the windows, or should the beds project from the wall at right angles, the head to the wall and the foot of the bed in the centre? This is not a question that can remain unanswered till the hospital wards are constructed, as it requires a differently shaped ward to house the same number of patients by the two methods. The normal way adopted in this country is for beds to be at right-angles to the walls, but in many cases seen abroad, our emissaries had seen the other method adopted, and some members of the planning sub-committee warmly advocated this plan, as it gives the patient the option of so lying in bed as to avoid having the light from any window in his eyes. The main objection to this plan, is that it is much less easy to nurse an acutely sick patient if the one side of his bed is closely adjacent and parallel to the wall, and this objection would be reinforced in the case of the teaching hospital, in that the bed would always need to be shifted if the patient were to be made fully available for examination and demonstration.

After much argument we compromised. In all the large wards of sixteen beds, the more usual British system was adopted; but in the small wards of twos and fours, the alternative method was instituted, as it was considered that these wards would be used mainly for the very sick patients, who would not be the subject of demonstration, and whose comfort should be the paramount consideration.

In the general layout, it was assumed that there would be 300 beds each for general medicine and general surgery, thirty for obstetrics, thirty for gynaecology, and a composite group aggregating sixty for the other special departments (ear and throat, eye, and skin). Nowhere were beds built specifically for paying patients, as it was assumed that they would be housed in a separate block which would occupy an adjacent site, to the east of the hospital.

It would be arranged for the dental work of the hospital to be carried out in the special department group, if the dental hospital did not come to the site at an early date as was expected. If so, it should be easy so to vary the internal arrangements as to turn over any beds allotted to dentistry, to other subjects.

In general, the instructions to the competing architects were that the internal arrangements of the wards were to be in such form that though they might have been intended in the first instance for a speciality, they could, at small cost be re-constructed internally to be adapted to general work if and when the corresponding special hospital came to the Centre site.

ANCILLARY WARD SERVICES

All of us who had worked in the older hospitals had suffered because there were no rooms near the wards where various ancillary services could be carried out. Usually the only ones were the ward kitchen and lavatories, though a patient's day room had often been included in the original plan. Most of these day rooms had long ago disappeared, having been used for extra ward accommodation or some other service.

We asked the architect to provide in immediate proximity to each ward unit, a larder, a ward kitchen, a sister's room, an examination room large enough to hold a ward class, a clinical room for students, a cloak room for visiting officers, a record room, day rooms, a small rest room for patient's friends, two reserve rooms, sanitary rooms, service rooms for cleaning apparatus, store rooms for bed rests, splints, sand bags, etc., and a room for patient's clothes to be stored when they came into hospital. A linen room completed the list (see diagram, page 87).

It was made clear that we also needed accommodation to be provided for patient's visitors, where in emergency they might have accommodation for the night.

86

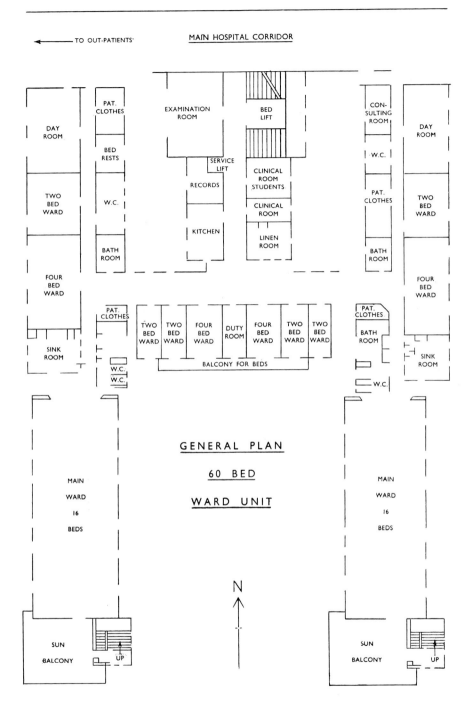

DIAGRAM OF THE LAYOUT OF THE WARDS

These rooms were to be largely adjacent, and all near the wards. Most of them needed little in the way of permanent fixtures, so that many of them might be interchangeable; in any case, the light walls which constituted their partitions, were carrying none of the structural weight, and could, if necessary, be swept away to increase the size of an adjacent room. What was necessary, in our experience, was to have a sufficiency of space available for these purposes, and for that reason, in the sketch plan that was drawn up, somewhat fancy names were given to the small rooms so to be constructed. I need hardly say, that the experience of those who are now managing the Queen Elizabeth Hospital is to the effect that we did not build a sufficient number of rooms of this character, or at least that we did not allow of enough space for the demands of 1952.

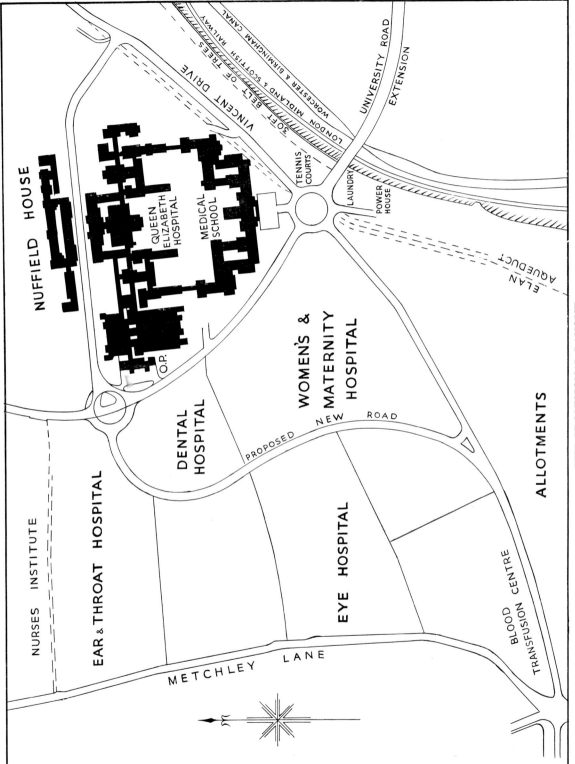

NUFFIELD HOUSE

QUEEN ELIZABETH HOSPITAL

MEDICAL SCHOOL

O.P.

VINCENT DRIVE

30FT. BELT OF TREES

LONDON MIDLAND & SCOTTISH RAILWAY

WORCESTER & BIRMINGHAM CANAL

TENNIS COURTS

UNIVERSITY ROAD EXTENSION

LAUNDRY

POWER HOUSE

ELAN AQUEDUCT

DENTAL HOSPITAL

WOMEN'S & MATERNITY HOSPITAL

PROPOSED NEW ROAD

ALLOTMENTS

NURSES INSTITUTE

EAR & THROAT HOSPITAL

EYE HOSPITAL

BLOOD TRANSFUSION CENTRE

METCHLEY LANE

THE PROVISIONAL LAYOUT
(1946)

CHAPTER XIX

HEAT, VENTILATION AND WATER SUPPLY

VISITORS to the old hospitals and infirmaries which were built a hundred years ago are often surprised at the height of the wards from floor to ceiling. In the Victorian days, it was generally believed that infection was spread by "miasmas", or airborne infections arising from a patient or even from refuse heaps and marshes. It was only when bacteriology became so generally recognised as to have informed other professions as well as our own, that it was possible to adjust our buildings to the new knowledge. We know now that infection from patient to patient can be averted in rooms of more modest dimensions, and that the lofty wards of the later Victorian years are not necessary to prevent the spread of such infective conditions as phagadena. Whereas in the old days, wards were built with a height of up to eighteen feet, we now know that there is no advantage to be gained if wards are more than some twelve feet high. No increased dilution of the "miasma" by the greater air space allowed for each patient is obtained, for the upper air of the high wards is largely stagnant.

At the General Hospital, designed in 1890, the wards had an average of sixteen feet; at the Queen Elizabeth, designed in 1931, the height is only twelve feet. It is thus possible to reduce building costs considerably without any loss of efficiency, or incurring any risk of an outbreak of infectious disease. Needless to say, adequate ventilation is essential in all hospital wards, and most of us have come to the conclusion that "natural" ventilation for the main wards is better than any of those special methods whereby the air, warmed, filtered and moistened is fanned into the wards by one series of ducts and is sucked out by another. It is difficult to say why this latter system is not acceptable, but our experience at the General Hospital was that although it saved much in the washing of bedspreads and other articles of ward furniture, the only patients who were advantaged were the elderly bronchitics and the asthmatics. Children did well for two or three days, but thereafter wilted and became lethargic, while most resident officers complained of headaches and loss of energy.

It was our experience at the General that determined us to revert to "natural" ventilation at the Queen Elizabeth, but we were anxious to avoid if possible some of the disadvantages of the usual form of radiators used for heating. The main objection to their use was that they projected into the ward, and it was difficult to keep the space at the back of them clean and free from dust; in addition, the smearing of the walls by convection currents rising above them, though probably not an indication of the risk of infection, was nevertheless a disfigurement to the ward. Add that the heat was often too great near the radiator and too little at a distance, and we were anxious to find some other method of heating the wards that would give us more even temperatures.

Some of us saw many buildings and hospitals that were panel-heated before we accepted this device. In this system there is a constant flow of hot water through a series of tubular panels, which are embedded in the ceilings; thus the heat is radiated downwards instead of rising by convection currents. Except in the nurses' home (Nuffield House), there are no exposed radiators, and even here it is only in the bedrooms that they are provided. By the panel-heating system, the water is heated in calorifiers in the power house, is pumped through the duct even to the most distant sections of the hospital, after giving off a branch to the Medical School. Arrived at each building, the water is carried by "riser" tubes to each floor, where it gives off branches to supply the various panels in the roof of each ward. After passing through the panel, the water is returned through tubes passing again to the calorifiers, having lost a few degrees of temperature in heating the wards and other rooms. It is thus a closed system of circulating water, and there is likely to be no risk of the deposition of such lime-salts as would tend, in time, to block the circulation.

Some of the buildings we saw made use of electricity to heat the water; this was a great advantage to a hospital, as it was almost entirely automatic in operation; if we could have adopted it at the Queen Elizabeth, it would have obviated the use of a power house; but it was only possible where "waste" electricity was available, after the main load had ceased to be needed by 6 p.m., and before 8 a.m. In one building, we were told the cost of the current supplied in this way was only one eighth of a penny a unit, for the electricity company were anxious to have available an outlet for their superfluous current at night.

As cheap electricity was not available for us, we were driven to build a power house; being in the close vicinity of a coalfield, we naturally adopted coal as the means of raising steam instead of the more expensive fuel oil, even though it did mean the adoption of a system which would involve the employment of more men in the engine house.

Writing in 1951, I believe it is true to say that the panel-heating system has been successful. The only snag has been that in two places where the building has slightly settled, there has been a shearing of the tubes as they leave the riser, with a resulting leak near the ceiling.

WATER SUPPLY

A large hospital uses a very large amount of water; with six hundred patients in an acute general hospital the amount required may easily reach a hundred thousand gallons a day, if we include all that is required in the laundry, the operating theatres and the auxiliary services. It therefore became important to be sure that such an amount was available at the cheapest possible price, subject to its being of the requisite degree of softness and entirely pure for human consumption. As it appeared to us that we could get a cheaper supply by so doing, we sank a well close to the boiler house. After some weeks of boring, delay being caused by our having selected a spot in which a large boulder had been deposited during the last Ice Age, we found a full supply at ninety feet; a test gave two hundred and forty thousand gallons of water in twenty-four hours, without any lowering of the level of the supply basin. This water was not perfectly pure, so we went deeper into the Keuper Sandstone, and at three hundred feet found water in bulk which was suitable from the point of view of purity, but was too hard for general use in the hospital. Eventually, the boring was continued to a depth of 450 feet, the last 150 feet being lined with perforated tubing while the rest was lined with normal tubes allowing no ingress of possible pollution from above the 300 feet level. Thereafter, the apparatus necessary for softening was installed, and eventually, as a reinsurance against pollution, a chlor-ammoniation plant in addition.

In order that we might have a sufficient supply of water in case of fire, and if for any reason the well-water failed, arrangements were made for two sources of supply from the city mains, one from University Road and the other from Metchley Park Road; in addition, a main was laid all round the hospital, so that hydrants could be installed at any point.

It was a great relief to all of us on the building committee that Mr. Harry Vincent was with us. His wide knowledge of the engineering side of business, and his ability to forecast both the cost of construction and of maintenance of the various forms of service possible to us, made our work much lighter than it would otherwise have been. The Executive Board, and indeed the Centre as a whole, are greatly indebted to Mr. Vincent for the way in which, over several years, he supervised the building of the engineering services.

———

CHAPTER XX

THE NURSES' HOME (NUFFIELD HOUSE)

WE were planning our nurses' accommodation in the years 1928 to 1931, and those readers who know only of the conditions of service of the nurses of today, will hardly realise the difference in their hours of duty, their education, and their accommodation, that have occurred since those days. Some of us, perhaps fortunately, were fairly certain that the change was coming, and would be upon us long before our hospital was obsolete. We did our best to ascertain from various other hospitals then in being how many nurses per hundred patients were likely to be necessary. The numbers suggested ranged from twenty-five nurses per hundred patients at one group of comparable hospitals, to nearly fifty at the most liberally supplied.

These were the days when nurses often worked for a 12-hour day, and when some if not most of the work now allotted to ward maids was done by probationers. We were hearing on all hands of the shortage of nurses, and of the numbers of them that "broke down in training".

I am afraid that at this stage I was one of the more awkward members of the building committee. I felt sure, from my own observation of nurses' service and the reports of others, and from the trend of public opinion, that all the figures which had been supplied to us from other hospitals and organisations interested in this question, would give us a hopelessly insufficient number of nurses. The reader must remember that we were building an "acute" hospital, in which the strain on the nursing service is always very great, for it was not anticipated that at any stage any material number of patients would be able to look after themselves, seeing that, early in their convalescence, they would be drafted to some convalescent home or, if circumstances were favourable, to their own homes.

The figure which we were eventually persuaded to adopt, worked out at sixty nurses for each 100 patients, so that for the 500 beds we were permitted to build in the first instance, the nurses' home would need to house 300. This home, now called Nuffield House after the generous donor of its cost, is an eight-storey building, containing separate rooms for each of 300 nurses; each room averages 110 sq. ft. in size, and contains a bed, wardrobe suitably fitted, and a radiator. It is interesting to note that these are the only exposed radiators in any of the buildings; it was believed that it would give the nurses the opportunity of adjusting the temperatures of their bedrooms to their own liking, and would also give them an opportunity to dry any garments that they wished, without displaying them to all and sundry outside their windows.

NUFFIELD HOUSE

94

In Nuffield House is the nurses' school. This group of rooms contains several class rooms, including those for practical demonstration, and a fine lecture theatre capable of seating an audience of 120; this lecture theatre, like all similar rooms, is largely sound-proofed, and has all the necessary equipment for projecting lantern slides and for the display of cinematograph films.

The matron is provided with special quarters, which include a separate entrance door, and accommodation for a guest. The sisters also have rather more accommodation than the nurses, and they, as well as the senior nurses, have special sitting rooms. A sick bay for eight nurses is provided on the first floor, and it need hardly be added that bath rooms, etc., have been provided on a generous scale. Two automatic passenger lifts are available.

The recreation hall is the most noteworthy feature of Nuffield House. When fully opened out, the hall will seat 1,000 people, and as it is largely sound-proofed, it provides an excellent room for concerts and large scale gatherings. The floor was so constructed that it might be used for dances, and, as I have been informed, it has proved to be entirely satisfactory for this purpose. Dividing screens usually separate the sections of the hall, so that it can be used for various purposes, such as sitting rooms, library, etc., for the nurses. The partitions reach to the ceiling of the hall, so that some degree of sound-proofing of the library and "silence" rooms is possible.

In the basement are the canteens, separate accommodation being provided for sisters and nurses. For mechanical reasons, due to the varying levels, it was found that the supply of food to these canteens from the main kitchen would be a slow and awkward service; it was therefore—with some reluctance on the ground of cost—agreed to use the adjacent basement floor—at this situation on the east side of the site above ground level—to provide a special kitchen to supply the nurses' home, and eventually, when it was built, the maids' home.

I believe there is no single item in our work upon which we, the building committee, have been challenged so often. The epithets used have been "stupendous", "colossal", "grossly extravagant", and in particular, it has been the recreation hall that has received most of the criticism. It is, or was, said to be wastefully extravagant to build a home for nurses that cost as much as £500 a head. The figure has been compared with all sorts of others, including that of building a house at that time. It should, however, be borne in mind that this was not a mere dormitory for nurses; it included all sorts of other accommodation, more particularly the nursing school; for we had in mind that this might well become a school for nurses, in the same way as our Medical School had developed.

I have mentioned earlier that our plans, including those for nurses, were drawn upon the basis of a 740-bed hospital. The intention in the first instance, had been to arrange for a separate home for the night nurses, as the noise inseparable from an active building containing some three hundred nurses and the maids and others required for their service, would be liable to interfere sadly with the nurses trying to sleep in daytime. The night nurses' home was to be attached to the main home, and on the west side; a short stairway gave easy passage from one to the other. We never got as far as determining the exact size of the night nurses' wing, for when the financial troubles of 1931-32 caused us to cut down the bed accommodation of the hospital from 750 to 540, it became clear that the whole nursing complement then required, could be housed in Nuffield House. To me, this was a great relief, for I felt sure that even then we had underestimated the number of nurses who would be required, and here was an opportunity to build for the present, and leave the future to be looked after by some other responsible body. The only stipulation we made, was that the accommodation in the inexpansible rooms, such as the recreation hall, the lecture rooms, and the canteens and kitchens, should even at this stage be built up to the full scale of the 750 beds.

Those readers who are interested in this subject may like to see the figures for 1951. Let it be understood that they refer to a general hospital associated with a medical school, where the patients are all of the acute type.

Today, the normal nursing establishment of the Queen Elizabeth Hospital, as is called the one which we were building, is a total of 649. This number includes a trained staff of 100, there being 549 "student nurses". Owing to the interlocking arrangements between the Queen Elizabeth and other hospitals, all of which are included in the Medical School group, the figure of 649 includes 60 student nurses for secondment to the General Hospital, the Children's and the Women's Hospitals.

Our figure of 60 nurses for each hundred patients ought to have been doubled to satisfy the nursing conditions of twenty years later. It is not to be wondered at that the first building change that had to be made by the United Hospitals when they took over, was to put up temporary accommodation for nurses; and that when the National Health Scheme came into operation, yet another temporary structure had to be added to house nurses.

CHAPTER XXI

NOISE

IF dirt and bacteria are the worst enemies in a hospital, noise comes a good second. For those who have been patients in a hospital, there is no need to stress this point; but for engineers and architects who have to build them, I should like to impress upon them the necessity of so making their plans that noise is eliminated as far as is possible. I have been in some hundreds of wards, have asked questions of some thousands of patients, and have been an in-patient myself on two occasions, and I am certain that so far as the patient is concerned, and it is his welfare that we should consider as being the most important, noise is one of the most distressing of his worries in hospital.

There are two types of noise to be considered, those made by others inside the ward and those from without. So far as the former are concerned, it is certain that we cannot get rid of all of them; the chattering of other patients, the conversation of doctors and nurses and such like, are sounds that can only be avoided in a single ward where no other patient is present. Much can be done to minimise the effect of these noises on the other patients in a 16-bed ward by the construction and the finish of the interior. A wall that is finished in hard plaster will reflect the sound to a large degree, and there will be some reverberation in a relatively small room; finish the walls in soft plaster, and see that they are not painted but only washed over with a distemper, and much of the sound is absorbed; the amount of reverberation will be small. If in addition, some part of the ceiling or the whole of it, can be finished in one of the acoustic plasters, the reverberation in a room of the size of our 16-bed ward will be trifling; unexpectedly, the ceilings are more important as sound-reflectors than the walls. Let me finish this note about walls and ceilings by saying that the lowest section of the walls must be in hard material, for otherwise the bumping of beds and persons against the softer material will inevitably cause early damage needing repair.

The floors of most of our best hospitals are finished with teak. This is a very hard wood, and stands any amount of wear; it is better than oak because the latter goes on shrinking from year to year, for centuries as one of my furniture friends tells me. In any case, oak is very much apt to shrink and warp in any conditions in which the room temperature may reach 80 degrees, and if anything goes wrong with the engineering control of temperatures, such troubles are to be expected.

Teak is the best of what I consider to be only a moderately good series of possibilities; we must wait till the manufacturer gives us something better before we change. Teak makes a very beautiful floor, but it fails us technically because it is slippery and relatively noisy. The ideal would be something like rubber, especially if it is never polished. This would give us a noiseless and non-slipping surface, but it fails badly when we consider the wearing qualities. Where it has merely to receive the impact of the ordinary shoe—without hob-nails—there is no difficulty; but if, as is done daily in most hospitals, the beds are dragged over the floor surface, the life of the rubber floor is so short that no building or managing committee will face the cost of maintenance. Linoleum occupies an intermediate position; it is not as a rule so attractive in appearance as either teak or rubber, but can be relatively non-slippery and it absorbs much of the noise made by those who walk on it. Needless to say, if a castor comes off a bed and it is dragged over either rubber of linoleum, it may quite easily cause a tear, whereas to a wood floor, it merely causes a scratch.

Carpets are banned as a possibility for a ward. They would be noiseless, or could be made so, but the difficulty in maintaining bacterial cleanliness would mean such frequent stoving that their life would be short. Various sorts of tiles are on the market, and for laboratories are sometimes excellent; but they fail for most wards because they will not stand the dragging of the beds over the flooring which is a process that we see no sign of eliminating.

External noises are another matter. Traffic on the roads can be heard in most of our hospital wards; it can only be minimised by distance, which means building the wards in the area most distant from the traffic node; curiously enough, this particular type of noise, if fairly continuous and not too intense, worries the patients very little. The noise made by lifts, in the opening and closing of the doors is very irritating, and this is a trouble that can only be eliminated by paying rather higher prices than most treasurers will face. Again, distance lends enchantment to the patient.

Noises made in the corridors are another external source of worry. In any big place, where a thousand people are working or being treated, there are bound to be noises, and they tend to be transmitted along corridors to a very considerable extent. Here the best way to minimise the trouble is to use as wall finishes some form of soft plaster; again, it will be necessary to finish the lower three or four feet of the walls in hard plaster or cement, lest the frequent bumps of ambulances, etc., should wreck the softer material. All ceilings should be finished in acoustics whenever the extra cost will permit, and above all, the floors of the corridors near the wards should be lined with rubber.

Another type of noise that is most irritating to the sick man, and even more to the sick woman, is that which is apt to come from the engineering services. Engineers are so used to noisy places that they do not notice the hum of a dynamo, whilst the still more objectionable air-locks that happen in even the best regulated establishments can be very distressing to a patient who would give anything to get to sleep. It is much better, if it can be so arranged, that the engines which provide the power for the heat, lighting and ventilation should be at a distance from the ward block, though usually this practice will mean that the cost of these services is increased.

There should be no telephone bells ringing in the wards. All incoming calls should be made by light signals; when I went into this question with the engineer, we found that by a series of five differently coloured lights, we could arrange for over a hundred individual calls to be made, and by adjusting a series of light signals in all likely positions, the telephone operator could give a call for any person likely to be wanted for the outside telephone. The corresponding telephone is located in the sister's office, so that if a doctor, working in the ward, is wanted urgently on the telephone, he can be called up within a few seconds. Note again, none of these call signals make any noise at all.

Many of the departures from previous practice were eventually adopted at the Queen Elizabeth Hospital. We were very anxious about noise, for all steel frame buildings tend to transmit noise made in one place to neighbouring wards. Above all, the noise made by the slamming of doors is transmitted in this way, and the modern generation which travels in cars is apt to express its personality and slam doors in exactly the same way that they shut the doors of a motor car. To a large extent, the soft plaster walls have reduced this conduction of noise, while the anti-slam devices that have been fitted to the doors in most places where necessary, have again made these transmitted noises a less irritating distraction. We fitted teak to the wards for flooring, but I yet feel that this is not the last word, and that our manufacturers will in time give us a less slippery and quieter surface, that will wear and look as well as teak.

A final word about building. The main cause of the transmission of noise in a modern large steel framed building, is that the materials of which the walls are constructed tend to constitute a sounding board; a steel framed building will always be noisier than one without steel. I still believe that if the builders of the future could so construct their walls that the steel is insulated from the brickwork by a layer of felt, or some similar material, the degree to which noise is transmitted would be greatly reduced. In the absence of any experience of such building when the Queen Elizabeth Hospital was constructed, no such device was incorporated; it is possible that what we amateurs are asking of the professionals is beyond the range of practical politics, but I should dearly like to see a steel framed building so constructed. The patient could then figuratively put his fingers to his nose at the door-slammer.

The normal way in which a nurse's attention used to be called to a patient in a large ward was by a shout either from the individual himself or from a neighbour. As we were deciding to fix up arrangements whereby all patients could, or need not, hear the wireless broadcasts, and as certain other services for each individual bed were needed, we decided to arrange for a series of gadgets to be available for each bed. In addition to the two already mentioned, a reading lamp, a plug for an inspection lamp, and another for the use, if necessary, of a heavy current for X-ray examination, was fitted over each bed. The nurse's call-sign was to show a red light over the bed where the call originated, and in the sister's room; only someone going to the bed itself could cut out the red light, so that it might be a glaring reproach to the nursing staff if it remained without attention. All calling by shouts was thus eliminated, and an extra contribution was made to the suppression of noise. We were greatly indebted to the consulting engineer, Mr. Fred. Lee, for the way in which the electrical devices were thus made available for each bed, for care had to be taken lest interference with the smaller currents needed for wireless were interrupted by the heavier ones used for X-rays.

———

CHAPTER XXII

ARCHITECTURE

APPRECIATION of particular objects as works of art, is a matter for individual taste; I am told that no court of law will assume the responsibility of determining what is artistic and what is inartistic. One nation approves one type, and another a different one; indeed the selection varies from age to age even in one country. There are, nevertheless, certain ways in which can be obtained an artistic effect which will meet with fairly general approval. We, the Hospitals Centre, were about to put up a large public building, and we all agreed on one point, that we ought to take pains to avoid disfiguring our city.

We were about to build the first of a series of hospitals and a medical school on a hundred-acre site. We were cheek by jowl with the Edgbaston section of the University, and we knew that extensions of the latter would shortly come nearer to our medical school. We were anxious to avoid that incongruity which is sometimes seen in our city, and we realised that so large a building as we were contemplating might become a blot on the landscape, and very much embarrass those who had to design succeeding buildings. Even in our own scheme, there were two different types of structure, one for a hospital and one for a school.

Always—first, last, and all the time—we had in mind that the building must be so constructed as to serve the best interests of the patients. We relied on our architect so to shape and mass the structure that such awkward features as the escape staircases, balconies and sanitary blocks became part of the whole design.

In order that there should be no clashing styles of building placed beside our own when the time came for others to be put up, we had a special clause inserted in our Memorandum and Articles to the effect that any new building erected on the site should first have its plans approved by the Centre; we hoped in this way to ensure that the same type of facing brick and the same general form of structure would be adopted for all the hospitals to come on to the Centre site.

We would have liked to build in Portland or Hollington Stone, or some similar material, but when we found that the extra price for what we needed would be in the region of two hundred thousand pounds, it became obvious that we must use cheaper materials, or we might condemn our successors who would need to build the other hospitals to such an expense that they would break away from the uniformity at which we were aiming.

We asked our architect to get his artistic effects from the massing of the buildings in their proper proportion, rather than from any external adornment. It was on the advice of Mr. Lodge that we adopted the "golden yellow-brown" facing brick, and before we had finished we were to use some four million of them. We had various samples tested at Teddington before we were satisfied to use them, for we had seen many facing bricks that perished and crumbled, to the destruction of much of the architectural beauty the building may have had previously. We also insisted on the use of cement mortar, for previous experience in this district had shown that lime mortar will not stand up to our atmosphere.

We hoped that when the first changes of a minor character became necessary, to meet the varying demands of a progressive art like medicine, it would be possible to avoid any damage to the shell of the building which largely determined its aestheticism; for this reason it was laid down that all partition walls, or at least as many as possible, should not carry any of the weight of the structure, but should be constructed of light materials which could be swept away at small cost.

I am no architect, and have no pretensions to educate the public on any question of art. Like most of us who have had a fairly general education, I have come to like certain types of pictures and buildings, and to regard them as expressions of art that satisfy me. If I am doubtful as to whether I like or do not like a particular object, I make it a practice to go and see it on several occasions; if its attractiveness grows upon me, I am content to believe that it is a type of art that I could live with comfortably. If, on the other hand, there is something which is merely pretty rather than beautiful, I find that successive visits tend to transform a possible liking into a positive distaste.

Judged in this way, I find that the mass of buildings that Mr. Lodge designed at Metchley is entirely satisfying. There is nothing pretentious about them, and the relative absence of adornment is to me attractive. The buildings appear to be exactly suited to the work for which they were built, and as the brickwork is now (1952) mellowing and the shrubs and trees we planted are growing, the colour scheme tones in excellently with the countryside. If and when the new "temporary" structures are swept away and replaced by suitable permanent buildings, the whole aspect of the Centre should be entirely pleasing. I advise anyone who would wish to study the general effect at the moment to stand on the railway bridge in University Road and look to the north, facing directly the Medical School; or perhaps still better take the view which Mr. Stanley Anderson shows so beautifully in the etching re-produced in the frontispiece, when looking north-west from the base of the University Tower. From both these view points, one is conscious of a satisfactory sense of mass and proportion, due to the materials used and the admirable treatment of the horizontal lines of the Medical School, so cleverly combined with the vertical lines of the hospital.

———

CHAPTER XXIII

EQUIPMENT

THERE were many items of the equipment and the finishes that we medical men were happy to leave to the equipment committee over whom Mr. Scott presided, with the help of the secretary, Captain Stone. This equipment included all the kitchen and laundry requirements, including in the former the rooms for refrigeration and preparation, and in the latter, the modern machinery for washing, drying and ironing some thirty thousand pieces a week. There were, however, one or two items in equipment in which we were particularly interested. Most of us will spend about a third of our lives in bed, and of our acute patients, few are likely to spend less than two-thirds of their stay in hospital in bed. It is therefore of the greatest importance to see that the beds are as comfortable as is possible under modern conditions, and some of us inspected and lay upon a whole series of beds before we eventually decided that the most comfortable available in 1935 was the "Slumberland" mattress, and which we persuaded the honorary treasurer to allow us to buy not only for nurses and residents, but for all the patients. It is my belief that one of the amenities for which the patients have been most grateful is the type of bed provided for them.

The screens for the wards, used for segregating a patient on occasion, were all of the noiseless type, another great boon in any big institution. One other item that deserves mention is the gas fire in each ward; it is not necessary for heating purposes, but constitutes a focus around which the patients, up for the first time, could congregate for tea and a chat.

CHAPTER XXIV

OUT-PATIENTS

PLANNING the out-patient department is one of the most difficult tasks of a hospital building committee. The troubles arise because not only is the number of special departments uncertain from year to year—they never seem to diminish in numbers—but the way in which patients are admitted is in process of change. Twenty years ago it was no uncommon sight on a Monday morning to have upwards of a thousand out-patients and their friends assembled in the waiting hall of the General Hospital, but many of the staff as well as many of our patients' representatives had been trying to reduce the numbers to more manageable proportions. If a physician or surgeon had to see fifty or on occasion as many as seventy new cases in a single morning, it became farcical to regard the work as being of the consultant standard. We therefore tried to make the out-patient work consultative, and after the institution of the panel system, this method was no great hardship to prospective patients. What we wanted to do was to introduce a system by which only a limited number of cases was arranged for any particular officer to deal with, and if they could be given a specific time at which to arrive and would keep to that time, it should be possible to eliminate altogether the large waiting room, with its pandemonium of sound and its risks of cross-infection.

At the time in 1927-28 when we were trying to find a way out of this planning trouble, the out-patient time-table on the lines suggested above was more of a hope than a reality. So far as immediate building was concerned, therefore, we were greatly pleased when it became possible to shelve the whole question, on the ground that in the early days at least, the new hospital should have no out-patient department of its own, but should rely on being fed from the existing extern departments at the General and Queen's; for the time being the patients would probably prefer using these clinics, as in the main they would be nearer to their homes.

CAR PARKS

Most of the hospitals in the country were built or begun before the motor car era; few of them have sufficient vacant land nearby upon which cars can be parked without unreasonable obstruction to other traffic. Today, so many of those who serve the hospital press for accommodation for their private cars, that serious congestion often results in the neighbourhood, and tends to make difficult the approach and temporary parking of the ambulances and omnibuses bringing patients and their friends to the hospital. This problem grows more and more awkward year by year as the motoring habit develops.

We were fortunate in having at our disposal a very large amount of space which could be converted into car parks. True the levelling and surfacing added to the expense of the building programme, but I believe that already there is a demand for more and yet more space for this purpose. At the same time, there is a demand from the various members of staff, that garages should be provided where the cars of resident officers—administrative, medical and nursing—may be safely housed.

Despite the provision that we made, and which is I believe, adequate for 200 cars, it often happens that the private approach road to the main entrance is lined with cars for almost its entire length. The demand for still more space for this purpose seems to be insatiable, and it is well that we were able to make such ample provision in the hospital precincts.

CHAPTER XXV

THE PROTAGONISTS

THE difference of opinion which became so clamorous about the Centre in the early 'thirties of the century cannot be understood by merely examining the minutes of committees and the press cuttings of that period. As I have indicated in former chapters, there had always been a reluctant acquiescence by a considerable minority to the establishment of a third general hospital rather than to the extension of the two existing ones locally. The needs of both those hospitals were urgent, and were becoming more and more unbearable year by year. The long delay in even getting our Memorandum and Articles of Association agreed by the Board of Trade, meant that there would be no relief for several years yet, and it was natural that when the explosion occurred towards the end of 1931, the main target for the attack should be the chairman of the board, Sir Charles Grant Robertson.

Grant Robertson was a man of outstanding ability, who would have made his mark in any profession. At the time when, in 1927, he became Chairman of the Executive Board of the Hospitals Centre, he was fifty-seven years of age. He was then Vice-Chancellor, formerly called Principal, of the University of Birmingham, and had been with us for some seven years; in this capacity he was the academic head of the University and Chairman of the Senate, a body which included among its members all the professors, including those in the Faculty of Medicine.

As a student at Oxford, he had had a brilliant career. He took a First in Greats (Lit.Hum.) and the following year a First in Modern History. After being Fellow and Tutor at Exeter College, he became Examiner to the University in Modern History and later a Fellow and Bursar of All Souls' College. He had made many contributions to modern history, and was generally regarded as an outstanding scholar when he was appointed Principal of the University of Birmingham.

At the time of his appointment to the Chairmanship of our Centre Committee, he was already well known to most of the men of light and leading in Birmingham, and of course, to those of us who were working at the hospitals attached to the Medical School. As his name implies, he was a Highland Scot. Though careful in money matters, he was never niggardly or mean, and this characteristic could be applied to him personally as well as to the disposition of the very large sums that came under his control as the Centre appeal funds flowed in. His lithe and active figure, and his long striding gait made him a conspicuous figure anywhere, and with his somewhat austere profile, he was the delight of the students who loved to caricature him. He had many friends who worked with him, or whom he met on occasions when he represented the University, but seldom did one hear of anyone who knew him so well as to call him by his Christian name without the prefix. Even after many years of close association, he always kept up the habit of addressing his heads of departments as "Dean" or "Professor" or by some such title, and there was rarely any relaxation of the formal and somewhat distant personal attitude.

He was one of those gifted persons who are able quickly to pick up the essentials of any subject, however new it might be to him. He had a barrister's flair for presenting a case, by marshalling the salient points and presenting them in their proper order to the audience. Until he was fifty years of age, it is probably true to say that his knowledge of a medical school or a hospital was a negligible quantity, but his position as Principal had informed him fully of the difficulties that were increasingly evident in the Medical School, and his membership of the boards of management of the two medical school hospitals, had given him an insight into the difficulties they were facing.

He was a fluent speaker and had an accurate verbal memory; he was never at a loss for the right word. He was at his best, as I always considered, in those speeches he occasionally made on the occasions of conferring honorary degrees upon distinguished men of letters, the arts, science or the empire. Not a word was out of place, and always the approbation was tinged with a sense of humour. He was never so happy as when he was lecturing. Given a little time to prepare, and a friend whom he could trust to give him the facts, he was able to address an audience upon almost any subject. On one occasion, he went to New York to try and get a contribution to our funds from the Rockefeller Foundation; it is credibly reported that after he had addressed the Trustees, one of them turned to a colleague and asked, "What is this man a specialist in, medicine or surgery"?

This capacity for lecturing, so valuable an asset in his work at the University, came near to being the undoing of the Centre. So much had it become a habit, that as chairman he would often open a committee meeting with a speech in parliamentary style lasting for half an hour. On one occasion, after an unusually long homily, one of the business men on the building committee, who had complained of "this waste of time", timed his next introductory speech at fifty-two minutes; he had not really completed his address, but as he paused for breath—not for lack of a word—someone jumped in with an interjection which interrupted the flow of beautifully rounded sentences in which he was instructing business men on matters of business. That evening, after the committee had ended, one of the lay members of the committee, with another at his elbow, asked one of Sir Charles' colleagues at the University if something could not be done to cut short these lectures, in order that some of the business men might have their say on such occasions. A somewhat tentative approach was made to the Vice-Chancellor, but it was evident that he took a poor view of the suggestion, and did not welcome the implied criticism.

With most of the medical members of the Centre committee, this tendency of the Vice-Chancellor to occupy the whole time of the meetings mattered little; with the business men and some others on the committee, of importance in the city generally and particularly to our hospital schemes, it was another matter.

Sir Gilbert Barling was Pro-Chancellor of the University, and as such was the business head and Chairman of the Council. He was one of the most prominent men of affairs in the city. He had been an eminent surgeon, one of the pioneers of aseptic surgery in the days when most surgeons were of the *laissez-faire* type and knew little or nothing of bacteriology. As professor of surgery, he had impressed all, students and colleagues alike, with his capacity for teaching and organising. He had been appointed to the position of Chairman of the Hospitals Council, an unusual position for any medical man, for it was organising ability that was the most important qualification. He had had, fortunately for Birmingham, an early training in business methods when, as a young surgeon, he had been the prime mover, with Sir John Holder, in the building of the "New General" Hospital in Steelhouse Lane.

To such a distinguished administrator, a lecture from Sir Charles, whether on the location of an operating theatre or on any matter of business, was regarded as being presumptuous. His lack of confidence in the chairman of the Centre was never made public, but those of us who were in constant touch with both were aware of the differences between the Pro- and Vice-Chancellors.

If the lack of affinity between the Pro- and the Vice-Chancellors was unfortunate, that of another Birmingham baronet was very nearly disastrous. **Sir Charles Hyde** was a wealthy bachelor, deeply interested in the University which had been founded by his revered friend, Mr. Joseph Chamberlain. He was the proprietor of the *Birmingham Post* and the *Birmingham Mail*, and other papers circulating in the Midland area. Although he never became a member of the Council of the University, he was the most generous of its patrons throughout the whole of his active life. In addition, he was deeply interested in the Queen's Hospital; for some years he had been a member of the committee of management, and at the time of the inception of our Centre scheme, he was president.

He took an active interest in the papers he owned, and in a general way directed their policy; any animosity he developed was apt to be reflected in his journals. Anxious as were both Robertson and Hyde to promote the interests of the University, temperamentally they were poles apart.

Where Grant Robertson never used a single word to express himself, if a paragraph could more gracefully define his meaning, Hyde revelled in economy of words. He was accustomed to conversing with business men who were rarely voluble in speech, and to whom the English language was merely a means by which ideas could be transmitted; to most of them, and particularly to Hyde, brevity and precision were what was wanted in informal conversation, and none of them had any use for the flowing periods of the Vice-Chancellor. Hyde came to regard the latter as a bemused theoretician, "intoxicated with the exuberance of his own verbosity".

Naturally, the two Sir Charles's, both deeply interested in the University, met on many occasions, and all sorts of stories were to be heard from students who heard—or said that they had overhead—the dialogue. One story was to the effect that when Robertson met Hyde for the first time after the latter had made a gift of £100,000 to the University, the former said, "Sir Charles, your generosity leaves me speechless". "A miracle", was Hyde's reply, according to some onlookers, though others invented less printable versions of the rejoinder.

In a general sense, we who were working on the Centre committee knew of these antipathies, but none of us realised till too late how they were to affect our progress. The medical men on the various committees were all more or less intimately connected with the University, and so had been trained to put up with lecturers who might be loquacious; with the business men, this method of speech was irritating in the extreme, and when, at a later date, the attack on the scheme started in the *Post* and *Mail*, there was ample ammunition for our opponents. The general attitude of business men was that a man who needed so many words to express himself as our chairman, could not be the man with the aptitude for carrying through a scheme like ours; to them, brevity was the soul of wit, and the essence of business. Slowly but surely, the antagonism to Sir Charles was translated into antagonism to the Centre Scheme itself, and if we had not had a stroke of fortune at that time, we might well have succumbed to the onslaught.

In 1930, **Mr. (now Sir) Harry Vincent** had joined us as honorary treasurer. He was what is usually called a "self-made" man, and had built up an enormous business as a toffee manufacturer. He had been a member of the Children's Hospital committee for some years, and had thus an insight into our voluntary hospital affairs. In addition, he had been largely responsible for the building of a large factory near the mouth of the Thames, and had directed the building of his own new and very beautiful factory at Hunnington. To most of us, he came as a comparative stranger, but very soon the whole committee came to appreciate his extraordinary ability in business, and to realise, as was said of him in a subsequent tribute, that in our new honorary treasurer, we had found a treasure. He rarely spoke in committee, but when he did, everyone of us realised that whatever he did say was worth hearing. He very quickly grasped what the medical members of the committee were aiming at, and heartily approved of the object of so building the hospital that it would combine the best possible treatment of the patients with medical education and research. From that time onwards, no one could shake his determination to see the scheme through, at whatever cost to himself. Indeed, though his chief recreation was yachting, when the time came for all of us to pull our weight to the full if we were to weather the storm, he, the master mariner who had sailed his yacht for many a hundred miles, sold the "Grey Mist", and gave up his beloved hobby.

Vincent was not a talker. When he got to know his new colleagues fairly well, he occasionally opened out and spoke his mind freely, but his comparative silence in committee served as an antidote to the volubility of the chairman. Above all, his presence as treasurer made the buiness men of the city come to regard the Executive Board as a body of men who might be expected to do something, for they agreed with Cecil Rhodes that a "bunch of Dons and Doctors" were as children in matters of business.

Even Sir Charles Hyde relented. When in 1937 he spoke at the First Annual Meeting of the United Hospital as their President, he said, "No great undertaking in this city ever made a worse start than the Hospitals Centre Scheme, nor a better recovery. Somebody made a fortunate discovery in Mr. Harry Vincent". From 1933 onwards the opposition in the *Post* and *Mail* died down, and we were fortunately able to carry on with the details of our work without the distractions caused by those who might have made the building of the hospital impossible.

Vincent's tenacity was made evident to me at an early stage of our association. We became close friends, and before long I was inveigled into accompanying him to see various buildings, either new or in course of erection; he made the excuse that he wanted me to support him in the committee, if any opposition were offered to what he had to propose. He knew all about building contracts, and how they might be framed so as to get the best results at the least cost; he must have saved the Centre very large sums of money by his careful control over the business of building. He insisted on a large series of sub-contracts being in the hands of the Centre, instead of such contracts being in the control of the main contractor, and it was in pursuit of alternatives which might be equally efficient and less expensive, that I had to accompany him on many expeditions. I well remember ruining a suit by climbing an eighty-rung ladder which was covered with fresh cement, at a building in the West End of London, just to see how the panel heating tubes were laid in a concrete floor; on another visit, this time to South Wales, it was types of flooring that we were to inspect, to determine whether they would satisfy our needs in wards or laboratories.

When the antagonism to the Centre Scheme was at its highest, and when it appeared that it was yet possible that we should be forced to return all the hundreds of thousands of pounds that we had collected, Vincent stood like a rock. "If", he said to me, "you will stand by me on the technical side, rather than see this scheme blown sky high, I will put up all the money necessary to build a 250-bed hospital, whatever anyone else may say". I knew that this would mean the end of my professional work for me, but we shook hands on the agreement. By good fortune, or perhaps some inkling of our determination had leaked out, the decision by the Lord Mayor's Conference, to whom had been referred the question as to whether we should proceed or not, reported in favour of our beginning the actual building on January 1st, 1933.

It was not only in the spending of our contributions that Vincent was such a tower of strength. Although we had an appeals committee, it was the energy and the personal appeals by Vincent that caused the fund to reach such stupendous heights. He made it his business to go round and see any of the possible donors who were

110

vacillating, and of course his position in "big business" in the city had brought him into contact with many of those who might have some surplus wealth available. It was this direct approach, and not any response to circular letters, which made possible the collection of over a million pounds, and although some of us did our best to help him, it was the personal influence and example of Harry Vincent that was the dominating reason for our success.

I never could be quite sure how much in actual money Vincent gave to our funds. I know it was over a quarter of a million, but I think that the greatest gift he made was of the whole of his time that could be spared from business, over nearly ten years, and the greatest sacrifice was that he ceased to roam the seas in the "Grey Mist". I know of no one who has ever given more devoted service to any charitable cause than did Vincent to the Hospitals Centre.

After the resignation through ill-health, of Sir Gilbert Barling, **Alderman William Cadbury** became chairman of the Hospitals Council. Already he had done much work on the City Council, and was well known as an outstanding member of a family which had done yeoman service to Birmingham. The hospital work that he had so far carried out, was as member and chairman of the Health Committee, which controlled the municipal hospitals. His appointment to the chairmanship of the Hospitals Council, set up to co-ordinate the work of all the hospitals, voluntary and municipal, was a fitting tribute to the work he had already done for the health of the city.

It was unfortunate that one of the earliest of his interventions in the affairs of the voluntary hospitals, the halting of their Extension Schemes, should have aroused the suspicions of many of the voluntary hospital representatives, that this was a move in the direction of municipalising the voluntary hospitals. Hints to the effect that such a policy was the aim of several prominent citizens, had been given privately on many occasions, though, as far as most of us knew, never in public. This uneasy suspicion was entirely removed when, in 1926 Alderman Cadbury announced the gift of the land which was to become the Hospitals Centre site. From that time forward, and afterwards when he was a member of the Executive Board and its building committee, Alderman Cadbury was a tower of strength. Not only did he devote much of his very valuable time to the work of the Executive Board, but by his personal generosity, and that of his family, his friends and associates in business, he greatly helped the collection of those funds which set a target for the whole of the Midland area. His influence with certain sections of the local press was unwavering in our support, even when the *Post* and *Mail* were fulminating against the continuation of the scheme.

It was a long time before many of us who were members of the committees became well acquainted with Alderman Cadbury, for his natural shyness, so unexpected in a man who had done so much public work, made it difficult for us to talk to him intimately about our aspirations and difficulties. Alderman Cadbury had been the first publicly to advocate the Centre Scheme, and the gift of the land, a hundred acres in exactly the right place to meet the wishes of the University as well as the hospital authorities, makes us regard him as the founder of our Hospitals Centre. It is a fitting monument to the work that he did, and to his generosity on so many occasions, that one of the main ward blocks of the Queen Elizabeth Hospital has been named after him.

Of the many medical men who served, the one who represented the Queen's Hospital in the earliest stages and has remained a member of the Board throughout, is **Dr. J. G. Emanuel.** He was chairman of the medical committee in 1931, and it was through his persuasion that his committee agreed to a General Hospital physician becoming Dean of the Faculty of Medicine, at a time when any break between the staffs of the General and the Queen's might well have proved fatal to the rebuilding of the Medical School. He was one of those who, at Alderman Cadbury's invitation, went abroad and inspected various hospitals, and brought back reports which helped us to decide on all sorts of technical questions.

Mr. John Scott had been in the postal service as head of the Birmingham office before he joined us. He came to us at a later stage most usefully, and was largely responsible for the equipment of the service rooms and kitchens.

Another representative of the General Hospital who remained with us throughout, was **Mr. Owen Thompson.** He was one of those who helped to prevent the difficulties at his hospital from crushing the Centre Scheme out of existence.

There were many others who, by their help on committees, or by gaining information from abroad and elsewhere in the British Isles, have helped us throughout the years of preparation and building. There are others who have helped more particularly in quelling opposition and by their advocacy inducing others in important positions in the city to refrain from overt criticism.

Of this group, one of the most important was **Mr. Sydney Vernon.** After some years on the Board of Management of the General Hospital, he accepted the post of chairman of the Hospitals Council after the resignation of Alderman Cadbury in 1937. He formed the "Vernon Committee" which was set up for the purpose of advising on the methods which should be adopted to bring into active use the new hospital; it was this committee which was largely responsible for the transfer from the United Hospital to a special committee of the Queen's Hospital building, to a new voluntary hospital which was incorporated, thus founding the Birmingham Accident Hospital which has been so outstanding a success.

The University of Birmingham is to be congratulated that so eminent a man of affairs has accepted the office of Pro-Chancellor, for with the rapid expansion now proceeding, his driving force and wide knowledge of business will be a great asset.

Mr. Harold Roberts, also a solicitor, and later to become a member of Parliament, was a very regularly attending member of the Executive Board. Throughout he was a forthright advocate of the Centre Scheme, and his devastating cross-examination of some of the critics was one of the factors which determined the "Lord Mayor's Conference" in 1932 to decide that the scheme should be continued.

Mr. Byng Kenrick was another ex-Lord Mayor of Birmingham, who had been deeply interested in education, and chairman of the city's education committee. He was a consistent advocate of the Centre, though his many other public services, including membership of the University Council, did not leave him sufficient time to become one of our inner cabinet. We could always rely on his help and advice in any emergency.

Throughout the preliminary discussions and the building period, we had no more staunch friends than the representatives of the Hospital Saturday and the Contributory Associations. If I were to pick out those who helped us most at the period of the controversy, I should thank **Mr. Bertram Ford**, later to become Sir Bertram Ford, who was in a difficult position as the business manager of the papers owned by Sir Charles Hyde; his work on the Contributory Schemes of Birmingham and elsewhere, made him well-known to all who were interested in our voluntary hospitals, for the enthusiasm he showed inspired contributions which so greatly helped the hospitals in the dark days of the 'thirties. His colleague, the secretary of the Hospital Saturday movement, was **Mr. Smedley Aston**, who never wavered in his support of the Centre Scheme, and who led the gallant band of works' representatives who supported us throughout.

There were many others who either directly as members of our committees, or by voluntary action in aiding our appeal helped us to carry our first stage of the work to a point where the first hospital could be opened and made available. Many of them will be mentioned by name in the section prepared by Mr. Burrow, where a list of those who served on committees is given. In case any of them should have by error been omitted, I hope they will here and now accept my apology, for the task of collating the list has been one of extraordinary difficulty.

No list of those who helped us would be complete without a mention of our secretary. **Captain J. E. Stone** was appointed on 8th December, 1928, and served throughout the whole term of the active period of the Centre's existence. He proved to be a very valuable officer, and was most economical in his office staff. Only when the work was at its maximum intensity did he ask for an assistant, and as the work included the appeal for funds which eventually brought in well over a million pounds, it will not come as a surprise to hear that the total cost of the office work was far below that normally met in similar circumstances; indeed over the whole building period the very small interest allowed by the banks on the amounts collected was nearly enough to meet the whole of the office expenses. In addition, his experience at St. Thomas' Hospital, and his wide knowledge of hospital finance and administration, were a great help to the Executive Board and the building committee, both in formulating their plans and in carrying them into effect.

We were throughout well served by our architect, **Mr. T. A. Lodge.** He was accustomed to designing big buildings, and the size and complexity of our Centre

Hospital proved to be well within his capacity. Always we knew that we could safely leave to him any decision as to the external appearance of the various buildings, but I am afraid some of us were a great trial to him at times when it came to internal deviations from the normal. He gave us a magnificently effective building, and if it is criticised by some as being rather too like a factory, it is not the fault of Mr. Lodge but of a committee who were determined to have an efficient hospital building, at whatever cost to its elevation. For myself, I should like to say that the external appearance of the buildings for which Mr. Lodge prepared the designs, seems entirely suited to its purpose, and that more ornate construction like those of the late Victorian period, are far less pleasing with their rather fussy ornamentation. I am satisfied that if the other hospitals to be built on the Centre site are constructed in the same external form and with the same type of facing brick, there will at long last be at least one section of our city where the architecture over a wide area is entirely in unison, and where the massing of great blocks of bricks and mortar is more pleasing to the eye than would be a whole series of more expensive buildings, each of which expressed the individuality of different architects.

Throughout our building operations, and even before we started work on the site, Mr. Lodge was a frequent visitor from London. Hardly a week went by without at least one visit, and his careful supervision of the details of the building was greatly appreciated. Those of us who were most intimately associated with him in the erection of the Hospital and the Medical School buildings, are deeply grateful to him.

CHAPTER XXVI

EPILOGUE

THE building of the first hospital on the Centre was ready for occupation on the last day of 1938, and on that day the "United Hospital", the name given to the amalgamated General and Queen's Hospitals, took over control and management. The accommodation actually provided for 540 beds, for the ward block which should have been the west wing was omitted for the time being. All the main operating theatres were completed, together with their supply room, in which the dressings and overalls are sterilised, and the anaesthetics are supplied directly to the theatres.

A few months after the actual commencement of work, Their Majesties King George VI and Queen Elizabeth graciously visited the hospital, and on that occcasion Her Majesty, now the Queen Mother, was pleased to name the hospital the "Queen Elizabeth" Hospital. Not only is this name a memento of a happy occasion, but it perpetuates to some extent the name of that other Queen's Hospital, founded a hundred years before and named by and after Queen Victoria, and whose staffs—medical, administrative and nursing—had been incorporated in the United Hospital which now administered the new hospital.

The years of war provided an excellent opportunity of testing out the newly-constructed Queen Elizabeth Hospital. Its position some two miles to the west of the centre of the city, resulted in its being largely immune from bombing, while the hospitals in the centre of the city were so frequently damaged that their complement had to be drastically reduced. The new hospital, built to accommodate 540 beds, with ancillary services for 750, expanded its complement to 1,000 and became the main central hospital for the Midland area. All admissions were acute cases, a large proportion of them needing operation. It speaks well for the flexibility of the construction that the Queen Elizabeth was able to extend its work so widely; all types of acute illness and damage were admitted, including civilians, air raid casualties, and members of the three fighting services.

It is a thousand pities that we were compelled by public opinion, as led by men of influence in national and municipal affairs in 1931, to curtail the building plans. As some of us expected, one of the first difficulties that arose was that there was insufficient accommodation for nurses, and in the restricted building period which followed the war, the only form of building permitted by those in authority was the slightly cheaper form in which the "temporary" nurses' quarters have been put on the site we reserved for out-patients and casualties. There has been a small saving, as I am informed, in the cost of constructing this dormitory by using the local red brick instead of the "golden yellow-brown" which faced the other structures in the Hospital and the Medical School. The result is exactly that ugly defacement which we took such pains to avoid, and which, for a relatively trivial sum, might have left the architectural elevation in much more pleasing form. True that the buildings are only "temporary", but he would be an optimist who is of opinion that this eyesore will be swept away in less than half a century.

To me, one of the omissions most deeply regretted, and caused by the controversy, is the refectory accommodation for the visiting staff. In these days of progressive specialisation, it is in the interests not only of the doctors but of the patients, that every effort should be made to break down the isolation of the specialisms into watertight compartments; a luncheon room in which there would be frequent if not daily contact between departmental heads and those who occupied similar positions in the Medical School, would have helped greatly in this direction. It is equally certain that the cutting out of the rooms intended for the teaching of the students in the hospital, will need to be remedied soon, if the education of the students in clinical medicine and surgery is to be maintained at a high standard.

Except that in both the hospital and the medical school, nearly every individual head of departments has said to me that he has not enough room, whilst his colleagues have been amply provided in this respect, I have heard few complaints; perhaps this is because my various colleagues, lay, administrative, medical and nursing, have been at pains to prevent one who was so largely responsible for the distribution of such space as we were allowed to build, from hearing of the defects for which we were responsible. Speaking from the point of view of the patient, for I have recently been an in-patient in the Queen Elizabeth Hospital for some five weeks, I am satisfied that in most respects the hospital comes up to our expectations. If there is still one criticism that I would offer, it is that we have not sufficiently eliminated all sources of noise, and that the lifts, and crockery at tea time both tend to worry a sleepless patient; the rubber flooring in the corridors has largely eliminated all noise made by traffic there, and it is only rarely that is heard the slamming of a door.

I remain an optimist for the Hospitals Centre Scheme as a whole. Although the progressive rebuilding of the other ex-voluntary hospitals is now no longer a matter wholly for local decision, yet the advantages of such a scheme with its close association with the Medical School and the Queen Elizabeth Hospital, would appear to make the reconstruction on this site an obvious development. In the same way, I should hope to see signs that the Institute of Nursing, which some of us think is a most important necessity for the not too distant future, will be built on the Centre Site. None of these developments is possible if the land-hungry municipality, or similarly acquisitive Government departments, are allowed to use for other purposes the land so generously given by the Cadbury family for hospital purposes, and which was guarded so jealously by the Hospitals Centre, so long as they had any influence in preventing its diversion.

116

APPENDIX A

THE EXECUTIVE BOARD

IN the list which follows are given the names of those who served on the Executive Board of the Birmingham Hospitals Centre, and the numbers of their attendances. Many of the members served for short periods only; the small number of attendances in certain instances is therefore no indication of lack of interest in the Centre.

Sir Charles Grant Robertson (Chairman) . .	79
Alderman W. A. Cadbury	62
Councillor Miss H. Bartleet	62
Alderman Harold Roberts	55
Professor L. P. Gamgee	10
Professor William Billington	38
Dr. Stanley Barnes	66
Dr. J. G. Emanuel	64
Mr. W. E. Adlard	26
Mr. W. Smedley Aston	50
Mr. E. P. Beale	26
Mr. C. E. Greener	37
Mr. H. F. Keep	56
Mr. T. H. Prust	46
Mr. C. E. Stephens	39
Mr. Owen Thompson	67
Mr. Frank Barnes	14
Mr. G. Hurford	22
Mr. A. H. Leaney	9
Alderman A. H. James	7
Professor J. C. Brash	13
Professor Seymour Barling	40
Mr. T. Oliver Lee	25
Sir Bertram J. T. Ford	16
Professor Sir Leonard G. Parsons	29
Colonel C. H. Howkins	17
Mr. E. J. Thomas	6
Mr. George Whitehouse	11
Mr. Hugh C. Aston	41

Mr. J. Sjogren	5
Mr. John Scott	27
Sir Harry Vincent	35
Alderman M. L. Lancaster	14
Mr. S. C. Mindelsohn	14
Sir Martin Melvin	16
Miss Doris Tippetts	30
Professor W. E. Wynn	25
Mr. Percy A. Abrahams	18
Mr. F. P. Gilhespy	4
Alderman W. Byng Kenrick	9
Mr. W. T. Fairfax	10
Mr. Bernard J. Ward	13
Major Gilbert Dennison	4
Alderman Sir John Burman	8
Dr. L. G. J. Mackey	11
Mr. H. J. Peart	5
Mr. John Glaisyer	14
Mr. E. H. Kenshole	9
Mr. E. Rainsford	1
Alderman A. H. Sayer	6
Mr. Gerald Lloyd	6
Mr. Frank Wain	7
Mr. G. Philip Achurch	9
Lord Austin	1
Mr. F. J. L. Hickinbotham	2
Professor H. F. Humphreys	4
Mr. C. E. Morgan	2
Mr. Sydney Vernon	2
Mr. C. E. Purslow	3
Mr. E. P. Hollander	1
Mr. R. L. Ekin (Solicitor)	2
Mr. H. H. Russell	1
Mr. J. F. Crowder	1

BUILDING COMMITTEE

The following served on the Building Committee of the Executive Board, the first meeting of which was held on October 9th, 1930, and the last on January 12th, 1939. The total number of meetings held was 51.

Sir Charles Grant Robertson	50
Sir Harry Vincent	50

Dr. Stanley Barnes	42
Alderman W. A. Cadbury	32
Dr. J. G. Emanuel	37
Councillor Miss H. Bartleet	36
Alderman Harold Roberts	34
Mr. John Scott	29
Mr. W. Smedley Aston	19
Mr. H. F. Keep	26
Mr. G. Hurford	28
Professor Seymour Barling	28
Sir Martin Melvin	19
Professor W. E. Wynn	29
Mr. W. T. Fairfax	34
Mr. Bernard J. Ward	21
Dr. L. G. J. Mackey	26
Professor W. Billington	2
Mr. M. G. Mendelsohn	6
Mr. T. Oliver Lee	1
Alderman Sir Ernest Canning	1
Professor J. C. Brash	1
Alderman M. L. Lancaster	3

As in the case of the Executive Board, some of the members of the Building Committee served only for short periods, and number of meetings attended is again shown at the side of each name.

APPENDIX B

CONTRIBUTIONS TO THE APPEAL FUND
1930 TO 1939

THE list which follows gives the names of those whose personal contributions amounted to ten pounds or more. Owing to lack of space, it is impossible to record the names of the one thousand two hundred and twenty-four subscribers, each of whom gave amounts varying from sixpence to ten pounds, or to offer individual acknowledgments to the thousands of Birmingham men and women whose contributions lie hidden in the consolidated amounts which appear under the name of such organisations as the Birmingham Hospitals Contributory Association.

The building of the Queen Elizabeth Hospital was only made possible by the co-operation, good wishes and generosity of all classes of the population. To all those generous and public-minded people, and to all those who made contributions in kind, the Executive Board of the Centre wishes to make cordial acknowledgment of their invaluable support; without that help, the first instalment of the scheme would have been impossible.

SUBSCRIBERS TO THE BIRMINGHAM HOSPITALS CENTRE APPEAL FUND

£	s.	d.	
250,000	0	0	Sir Harry Vincent, LL.D.
198,000	0	0	The Rt. Hon. Viscount Nuffield, LL.D.
100,000	0	0	Messrs. Cadbury Bros. Ltd.
40,000	0	0	The Birmingham Hospitals Contributory Association.
30,000	0	0	Sir Charles Hyde, Bart., LL.D.
29,255	0	0	George Squires, Esq. (Legacy).
26,732	0	0	Mitchells & Butlers Ltd.
25,000	0	0	A. E. Hills, Esq., B.SC.
23,000	0	0	The W. A. Cadbury Trust.
21,000	0	0	The Austin Motor Co. Ltd.
21,000	0	0	Sumner's Typhoo Tea Co.
20,000	0	0	Members of Departments of Birmingham Corporation.
18,000	0	0	Alderman W. A. Cadbury, LL.D.
16,000	0	0	Mr. and Mrs. Barrow Cadbury.
15,000	0	0	The Trident Trust, per Walter Barrow, Esq.
15,000	0	0	Tube Investments Ltd.
12,093	0	0	Sir William Waters Butler, Bart.

120

£	s.	d.	
12,000	0	0	Ansells Brewery Ltd.
12,000	0	0	Birmingham and District Association of Master Bakers, Confectioners and Caterers.
12,000	0	0	Sidney C. Harrison, Esq.
12,000	0	0	Joseph Lucas Ltd.
10,385	0	0	Sir Peter Bennett.
10,000	0	0	Baron J. Davenport, Esq.
10,000	0	0	Davenport's Brewery Ltd.
10,000	0	0	Dunlop Rubber Co.
10,000	0	0	The John Feeny Charitable Trust.
10,000	0	0	Councillor Walter Higgs.
5,500	0	0	Cadbury Bros. Charitable Trust.
5,500	0	0	Miss Dorothy Cadbury
5,000	0	0	The Rt. Hon. Lord Austin.
5,000	0	0	Wilfrid Hill, Esq.
5,000	0	0	Imperial Chemical Industries Ltd.
5,000	0	0	Douglas James, Esq.
5,000	0	0	George Mason, Esq., Mrs. B. N. Lloyd and Mrs. M. E. Lowe (Joint contribution)
5,000	0	0	E. L. Payton, Esq.
5,000	0	0	Brotherton & Co.
4,003	2	3	Birmingham Hospitals Centre Bed Equipment Fund (per Mrs. G. Pearson, Hon. Treasurer).
3,500	0	0	Alfred Bird & Sons Ltd.
3,150	0	0	Britannic Assurance Co. Ltd.
3,000	0	0	General Electric Co. Ltd., Witton. Alderman J. H. Lloyd, J.P.
2,500	0	0	H. A. Butler, Esq. Mr. and Mrs. Edward Cadbury.
2,435	5	11	Residue of Estate of John Collins, Esq.
2,340	0	0	Albright & Wilson Ltd.
2,250	0	0	Birmingham and District Butchers and Pork Butchers Trade and Benevolent Association.
2,200	0	0	W. Canning & Co. Ltd.
2,140	0	0	Birmingham Wholesale Fruit and Vegetable Merchants' Association.
2,000	0	0	Lewis's Ltd. Hugh Morton, Esq., J.P. Southall's (B'ham) Ltd. Bell & Nicolson Ltd.
1,935	0	0	Mr. and Mrs. Gerald W. Kenrick.
1,811	2	10	Birmingham Corporation Tramways and Omnibus Department.
1,605	15	5	Bournville Works Men's and Women's Councils.
1,561	5	2	King's Norton Ward Appeal Committee.
1,400	0	0	Walter Barrow, Esq., LL.D. C. Kunzle Ltd. Edward Grey Ltd.
1,355	0	0	Councillor and Mrs. F. G. Whittall.
1,350	0	0	Birmingham Rotary Club and Philip W. Mitchell, Esq.
1,290	0	0	Anonymous. Sir John E. Mitchell. Alderman W. Byng Kenrick.
1,250	0	0	George Ellison Ltd. H.P. Sauce Ltd. H. F. Keep, Esq., J.P.
1,244	13	9	Birmingham Hospitals Council.
1,151	19	4	City of Birmingham Police Force.
1,100	0	0	Thomas Barclay, Esq. Midland Counties Dairy Ltd. William Newman & Sons Ltd. C. F. J. Tranter, Esq. Harry Payne Ltd. Edwin White, Esq.
1,052	10	0	G. F. Heath, Esq.
1,050	0	0	Birmingham Co-operative Society. Joseph Cohen, Esq. Mathew H. Clark and

£	s.	d.	
1,050	0	0	Councillor Mrs. Clarke. Foster Bros Clothing Co. Ltd. Colonel Frank Marsh. John Powell, Esq. Wilkinson & Riddell Ltd.
1,000	0	0	Geo. S. Albright, Esq., J.P. Ash & Lacy Ltd. W. A. Albright, Esq. Sir Fitzroy and Lady Anstruther-Gough-Calthorpe. W. & T. Avery Ltd. Birmingham Battery & Metal Co. Ltd. Dr. Stanley Barnes. C. Bryant & Sons Ltd. James Booth & Co. (1915) Ltd. *Birmingham Gazette* and *Evening Despatch.* Mr. Frank Barnes. Bellis & Morcom Ltd. Dame Elizabeth Cadbury. C. W. Cheney & Son Ltd. Ernest R. Canning, Esq. Mr. and Mrs. George Cadbury. Mr. and Mrs. Paul Cadbury. Frank Davenport, Esq. Ernest Edmonds, Esq. Evered & Co. Ltd. C. R. F. Englebach, Esq. General Electric Co. Ltd., Witton (Employees' Benevolent Fund). Trustees of C. F. Gare. Sir Thomas Gooch, Bart. Harrison (Birmingham) Ltd. Alfred Hughes & Sons Ltd. Halford Cycle Co. E. C. Keay, Esq. Arthur A. Kohn, Esq. Oliver Lucas, Esq. Alderman J. H. Lloyd, J.P. McKechnie Bros. Ltd. Richard Mealings, Esq. J. M. Nicolson, Esq. "O.K." Pinchin Johnson & Co. Ltd. Colonel A. J. Rabone. Alderman J. H. Sayer, J.P. Southall Bros. & Barclay Ltd. Douglas W. Turner, Esq. "T.E." J. R. Turner, Esq., J.P. Sir Walford H. Turner. Wesleyan & General Assurance Society. T. Walker & Sons Ltd. John Wright & Co. Colonel J. H. Wilkinson, D.L., J.P.
750	0	0	Mr. and Mrs. Edward Evershed.
702	15	3	Birmingham Hospitals Saturday Fund.
700	0	0	Val de Travers Paving Co. Ltd. Rt. Hon. J. W. Wilson. Miss Ruth Nettlefold.
650	0	0	Edmund P. Beale, Esq.
645	0	0	W. Owen Butler, Esq.
626	5	0	Frederick Smith Ltd.
600	0	0	William Bulpitt & Sons Ltd. Mr. and Mrs. H. A. Dugard.
599	12	0	Greyhound Racing Association
575	0	0	Birmingham Dental Hospital (Honorary Staff).
550	0	0	Employees of Benton & Stone Ltd.
525	0	0	Henry Hope & Sons Ltd.
510	0	0	Ten Acres and Stirchley Co-operative Society.
501	12	3	Henry Wiggin & Co. Ltd.
501	0	0	Birmingham Business & Sportmen's Club.
500	0	0	Anonymous. Atkinsons Brewery Ltd. Anonymous. L. Antweiler, Esq. T. Ansell, Esq. Anonymous. "S.A." Estate of the late Edward Butler, Esq. Benton & Stone Ltd. Bank of England. Barclays Bank Ltd. R. H. Butler, Esq. Anonymous. Co-operative Wholesale Society Ltd. (Manchester). C. W. Cheney, Esq. L. J. Cadbury, Esq., O.B.E. Major J. H. Cartland. Anonymous. The Right Hon. Neville Chamberlain, M.P. Fentham's Charity. Mr. and Mrs. J. H. Francis. William B. Gibbins, Esq. John Gibbins, Esq. C. B. Holinsworth, Esq. George Jackson & Co. Sir Barry Jackson. J. Archibald Kenrick, Esq. Lloyds Bank Ltd. Harry Lucas, Esq. George J. Mason Ltd. Midland Bank Ltd. National Provincial Bank Ltd. Palethorpes Ltd. Mr. and Mrs. R. A. Pinsent. Edward Webb & Sons (Stourbridge) Ltd. Lieut.-Colonel Walter W. Wiggin. Wrights Ropes Ltd. Mr. and Mrs. John B. Whitehouse. Mr. and Mrs. A. H. Wiggin. Mrs. Minnie C. Smith. Dr. T. Stacey Wilson.
479	16	8	Employees of Benton & Stone.

122

£	s.	d.	
455	0	0	Charles Clifford & Son Ltd.
450	0	0	Miss Hilda M. Inge. Mrs. Hannah Taylor.
434	7	9	Louisa Green (Legacy).
431	11	1	Wireless Appeal by the Rt. Hon. Neville Chamberlain, M.P.
400	0	0	Alderman and Mrs. Ernest Martineau.
377	10	7	Birmingham University Guild of Graduates.
350	0	0	Barker & Allen Ltd. A. E. Gyde, Esq. Mr. and Mrs. H. E. Parkes. James Moffat & Sons. F. W. Rushbrooke, Esq.
325	0	0	Professor W. H. Wynn.
310	0	0	Professor and Mrs. Seymour Barling.
302	10	0	Sharp, Parsons & Co.
301	11	11	Workpeople and Staff of Mitchells & Butlers Ltd.
300	0	0	Anonymous. Estate of the late Hugh P. Raikes, Esq. William Tangye, Esq.
292	10	0	Gerald B. Lloyd, Esq.
291	11	0	Councillor and Mrs. O. Morland.
285	11	8	Proceeds of Celebrity Concert (per Andrew Clayton, Esq.).
276	5	0	Thomas Smith & Sons (of Saltley) Ltd.
262	10	0	Trustees of the Cregoe Colmore Estate. S. C. Larkins & Sons Ltd. Mander Bros. Ltd.
260	0	0	Brown, Hopwood & Gilbert Ltd.
255	5	0	Philip A. Rodway, Esq.
250	0	0	Charles F. Barwell, Esq. Beacon Insurance Co. Ltd. C. E. Keep, Esq. Gibson & Ashford Ltd. John Jones, Esq. Richard Lunt & Co. Ltd. Fred. M. Lea. Leo Myers, Esq., O.B.E. Newey Bros. Ltd. Thomas Piggott & Co. Ltd. Stourbridge Glazed Brick & Fireclay Co. Ltd. Showells Brewery Co. Ltd. Eric W. Vincent, Esq. Westminster Bank Ltd. J. Edward Wilcox, Esq. Walter E. Wilson, Esq. William J. Wilson, Esq. F. W. Woolworth & Co. Ltd.
240	0	0	Boxfoldia Ltd.
225	0	0	Barrows Stores Ltd. Harris & Sheldon Ltd.
215	1	0	Paramount Theatre Ltd.
210	0	0	Alderman Sir John Burman. M. Howlett & Co. Ltd. Slough Estates Ltd. South Staffordshire Waterworks Co. Ltd. C. Herbert Smith, Esq.
200	0	0	Bousfield Bros. Bocks Trust Committee. Birmingham and Midland Scottish Society. Birmingham & Midland Motor Omnibus Co. Ltd. Sir Gilbert Barling, Bart. Miss Hannah H. Cadbury. Richard I. Dawson, Esq. Excelsior Philanthropic Society. Alderman and Mrs. M. L. Lancaster. Edwin Marshall & Son. Pearce & Cutler Ltd. Pattison-Hughes Catering Co. Ltd. Mrs. H. J. Rabone. Owen W. Thompson, Esq. Mr. and Mrs. H. Lloyd-Wilson. Mr. and Mrs. Musgrave Woodman.
196	3	10	Birmingham and Midland Counties Grocers' Protection and Benevolent Association
188	12	0	Members of the Birmingham Fish, Game and Poultry Dealers' Association.
187	18	0	Knights of the Empire Fellowship.
175	0	0	Sir Leonard and Lady Parsons. Sir Beckwith and Lady Whitehouse.
157	0	0	Colonel Sir Bertram Ford, T.D., D.L., LL.D.
155	0	0	British Industrial Plastics Ltd. Callenders Cable & Construction Co. Ltd. Employees of Parker, Winder & Achurch Ltd. Arthur S. Potts, Esq.
150	0	0	Birmingham Railway Carriage & Wagon Co. Ltd. (Employees' Administration Fund). Employees of Walter Somers Ltd. A. H. Stephenson, Esq. W. H. Smith & Co. Ltd. Mrs. Lionel Spiers.

£	s.	d.	
140	0	0	The Right Hon. The Earl of Bradford.
135	5	0	Mr. and Mrs. G. A. C. Pettitt.
135	0	0	Alderman T. O. Williams. Mr. and Mrs. Kenneth H. Wilson.
131	8	5	Birmingham Jewellers and Silversmiths' Association.
131	8	0	Councillor Frederick Mountford.
129	0	0	John and E. Sturge Ltd.
127	10	0	Parker, Winder & Achurch Ltd.
126	5	0	Alderman Sir Frederick Smith, J.P.
125	0	0	Anonymous. W. H. Briscoe & Co. Ltd. W. F. Bridgwater & Scurragh.
121	0	0	C. H. Allock, Esq.
120	0	0	Morris & Shaw Ltd. E. Marston Rudland, Esq. County Borough of Smethwick (Sunday Cinema Fund). Miss E. A. Taylor.
115	10	0	J. A. Jefferson, Esq. Sir James and Lady Curtis.
114	16	11	Rudge Whitworth Ltd. (Employees of Tyseley Works).
110	10	0	Mrs. Richardson Evans. E. C. Morris, Esq.
110	5	0	Professor W. Billington.
109	0	0	Birmingham Olympiad.
105	5	0	Midland Educational Co. Ltd.
105	0	0	Anonymous. Mr. Stirk Adams. Alexander Theatre. Birmingham Parks and Cemeteries Dept. Miss Margaret E. Backhouse. Dr. Harold Black. Alderman and Mrs. J. B. Burman. Cannock Chase Coal Owners' Association. Corn Products Ltd. C. H. Collins & Sons Ltd. J. G. Chidlaw, Esq. Docker Bros. Ltd. Ludford C. Docker, Esq. Davis & Mawson Ltd. Professor J. G. Emanuel. Ellis & Co. (Birmingham) Ltd. F. B. Goodman. Dr. A. D. Heath. Mr. R. Beatson Hird. J. Lyons & Co. Ltd. Mr. B. Lloyd. Dr. L. G. J. Mackey. Mr. F. D. Marsh. Edgar E. Lamb, Esq. Municipal Officers Guild. Midland Electric Corporation for Power Distribution Ltd. M. Myers & Son Ltd. Mr. G. P. Mills. Francis Nicholls Ltd. A. J. Norton & Son Ltd. Sir Francis H. Pepper. Dr. C. E. Purslow. A. J. Potts, Esq. Sir Hanson Rowbotham. Royal Warrant Holders' Association. Reckitt & Son Ltd. Round Oak Works Ltd. Charles Rainsford, Esq. Stoneware (1928) Ltd. M. H. H. Sampson. Mr. and Mrs. C. H. Sanders. G. D. Swiffen, Esq. Dr. Harold Thwaite. Dr. A. P. Thomson. Frank Taylor, Esq. Edgar Washbourne, Esq. John White, Esq. R. F. White, Esq. Professor K. D. Wilkinson. Mr. B. J. Ward. Mr. and Mrs. Henry Walters.
104	2	7	Employees of Kalamazoo Ltd.
102	2	0	W. R. Blanchard, Esq.
100	13	7	Staff and pupils of Yardley Secondary School.
100	0	0	Allday Ltd. Employees of Albright & Wilson. Anonymous "U". Anonymous. Anonymous (Medical Staff Queen's Hospital). W. E. Adlard, Esq., J.P. Mr. and Mrs. J. Herbert Ashton. Bendix Ltd. Batchelor Robinson & Co. Ltd. Best & Lloyd Ltd. Dr. Clement Belcher. W. Butler & Co. Ltd. H. W. Bainbridge, Esq. Mrs. Alice Beale. Councillor H. K. Beale. A. B. Bennett, Esq. Percy W. Cox Ltd. Brandon Cadbury, Esq. G. H. Collingwood, Esq. Darby & Co. Charles Darby, Esq. Electrical Components Ltd. F. Edmonds, Esq. Sir Walter Fisher, J.P. Mr. and Mrs. Henry C. Gibbins. John Gibbs, Ltd. Miss Emma Gibbins. Mr. John Gibbins. Ralph W. Hope, Esq. Sidney Hirst, Esq. Halesowen Steel Co.

£	s.	d.	
100	0	0	Frank Hawker, Esq. Holbrooks Ltd. Howard Hughes, Esq. William Charles Howard, Esq. Miss Sarah Hadley. Hale & Lane Ltd. Frank Holliday, Esq. R. M. Hewitt, Esq. Henry Hyde, Esq. Ingall, Parsons, Clive & Co. Ltd. Isaacs & Co. Isaac L. Jacobs. Joseph James, Esq. and Miss James. Mr. and Mrs. Russell Jolly. Israel L. Lyons, Esq. Randle Lunt. Lichfield Municipal Charities. T. Oliver Lee, Esq. Rev. Canon A. G. Lloyd. Richard Lunt, Esq. Dr. Isabel Martineau. Mrs. Mary T. Mackenzie. George Morgan Ltd. F. J. Mealings. R. W. Mealings. Meredith Turner & Co. Councillor G. F. MacDonald, J.P. George E. Neale, Esq. W. H. Owen, Esq. George A. Pope, Esq. Mr. and Mrs. Edward Prosser. John H. Pearson, Esq. Sir Patrick Hannon, J.P. R. Partridge, Esq. E. C. Paskell, Esq. Mrs. George H. Pearson. Jack Pickard, Esq. Miss K. P. Rushbrooke. John Reynolds & Sons Ltd. Mrs. Sabin. F. R. Simpson & Co. Ltd. A. H. Sayer Esq. F. F. le Souff Simpson, Esq. Stanford & Mann Ltd. St. John Ambulance Brigade (B'ham Corps No. 3 District). Alderman Frank Smith. Alfred Southall, Esq. "Two Grateful Patients". C. Douglas Terry, Esq. Triplex Foundry Co. Ltd. Van Houten Ltd. Webley & Scott Ltd. Mr. and Mrs. A. H. Warriner. Mr. and Mrs. Anthony L. Wilson. Baron R. Walker, Esq. Dr. J. Christopher Wilson.
96	10	0	Miss S. J. Knight (Legacy).
94	10	0	Charles Wright, Esq.
94	6	8	Birmingham Dental Hospital (Committee, Staff and Employees).
92	12	0	G. W. Ashford, Esq.
88	10	10	Clerk to the Justices and Staff.
83	0	0	Town Mills Ltd.
78	15	0	Birmingham and District Mineral Water Manufacturers' and Bottlers' Association Ltd.
76	5	0	Alderman and Mrs. Harold Roberts.
75	0	0	Mr. and Mrs. C. W. Gillett.
73	10	0	Midland Tar Distillers Ltd.
70	0	0	Dr. T. L. Hardy. Harry G. Jones, Esq. G. A. Laughton, Esq. Albert James Teall, Esq.
67	9	0	Birmingham and Five Counties Architectural Association.
63	0	0	Edgar Rainsford, Esq.
62	10	0	C. E. Bateman, Esq.
60	0	0	Employees of Triplex Safety Glass Co. Ltd.
58	5	9	Exhibition of Royal Photographs.
56	3	0	Birmingham and District Medical Women's Association.
57	0	0	Leonard Southall, Esq. The Three Nineteens (per M. G. Mindelsohn, Esq.).
56	0	0	Dr. H. W. Featherstone.
55	5	0	C. S. Wilkinson, Esq.
52	10	0	Dr. and Mrs. Bulmer. Dr. J. F. Brailsford. Caxton Floors Ltd. Mr. A. B. Danby. England & Sons. Edwards, Son & Bigwood. Fisher & Ludlow (1920) Ltd. Garton, Sons & Co. Ltd. Mr. and Mrs. George Goodwin. Mr. W. Gimmill. George H. Hughes, Esq. Employees of Hall & Lane. George H. Heath, Esq. Horatio Lane, Esq. Morland & Impey Ltd. The Mint (Birmingham) Ltd. Mather & Crowther Ltd. Employees of Midland Tar Distillers Ltd. Dr. R. P. Scott Mason. Major T. B. Pritchett. The Rocket Club. Austin Reed Ltd.

£	s.	d.	
52	10	0	Dr. C. A. Raison. Mr. C. Rudd. Spicers Ltd. Dr. J. M. Smellie. Mr. F. A. R. Stammers. Mr. J. N. Sankey. Dr. C. G. Teall. James Upton Ltd. Charles Wade & Co. Ltd. Charles Winn & Co. Ltd. Professor Haswell Wilson.
52	0	0	Dr. Helen Mason.
51	9	0	Charlton & Co.
50	0	0	Anonymous. Mrs. G. W. Ashford. Anonymous. Archbishop of Birmingham, The Very Rev. Thomas L. Williams. Dr. E. W. Assinder. Birmingham Jewish Literary & Arts Society. Birmingham Electric Furnaces Ltd. E. D. Barclays, Esq. W. Bulpitt, Esq. Burt Bros. Ltd. Birmingham Coffee House Co. Ltd. Mrs. M. A. Bell. Birmingham Stock Exchange. Dr. W. E. Barnie-Adshead. Dr. O. Brenner. Thomas Burman, Esq. Mrs. Winifred Cook. Carron & Co. Ltd. Sir Cornelius Chambers. Dr. P. C. P. Clarke. S. N. Cooke, Esq. Dr. Hugh Donovan. J. Jameson Evans, Esq. Arthur E. Evans, Esq. P. J. Evans, Ltd. Mr. and Mrs. E. Elliott. Oliver Essex, Esq. Frank H. Evans, Esq. Howard Fisher, Esq. W. H. Griggs, Esq. Mrs. C. H. Griggs. Alderman S. J. Grey. Dr. T. S. Grieves. Charles Hackwood, Esq. Mrs. M. A. Homer. O. C. Hawkes Ltd. Richard Jones Ltd. Mrs. Caroline James. C. Upfill Jagger, Esq. John Keatley, Esq. Harry Lainsdale, Esq. Conway Lowe, Esq. Lees & Sanders Ltd. Mrs. Elizabeth McDonald. Stanton G. Marsh, Esq. Midland Electric Manufacturing Co. Ltd. J. P. Morrison, Esq. W. H. Newton, Esq. Sir Francis A. Newdegate, G.C., M.G. The Priory Tea & Coffee Co. Ltd. "Past Member of Hon. Medical Staff— Queen's Hospital". M. A. Rollason, Esq. T. H. Ryland, Esq. A. W. Pearce, Esq. C. B. Robinson, Esq. William Robinson, Esq. Mr. B. T. Rose. Shirley Carnival. Gilbert Southall, Esq. Sperryn & Co. Mr. W. Arthur Smith. C. Southall, Esq. Charles Taylor (Birmingham) Ltd. Mr. and Mrs. Allan Tangye. E. Lancelot Turner, Esq. Walpamur Co. Ltd. Mr. and Mrs. Frank Wain. W. C. Webster, Esq. Mrs. James Whitfield. J. W. Wilson & Sons. M. A. Wolff, Esq.
47	19	4	"B.C. and E.C."
47	8	5	John Rae, Esq.
42	0	0	Mr. and Mrs. W. H. Carr.
40	2	2	Employees of J. A. Reynolds & Co. Ltd.
40	0	0	J. W. Marshall, Esq. Three Arts Ball.
38	18	7	County of Birmingham Ranger Guides and Rover Scouts.
37	16	0	Staff of Northern Assurance Co., Colmore Row.
36	15	0	Sir Frank Wiltshire. Crook & Riley Ltd. Horrell & Bowman Ltd.
36	0	0	Alfred Aston. Exors. of the late R. Woolcot, Esq. and R. W. A. Mullins, Esq. (Joint contribution).
35	10	0	W. F. Southall, Esq. Arthur H. Wolseley, Esq.
35	0	0	Arthur M. Bartleet, Esq. J. Holtham Cadbury, Esq. Dr. L. T. Clarke. Arthur Finney, Esq. Hampton Works Co. Councillor W. W. Longford. Miss E. M. Lloyd.
34	14	1	Institute of Transport.
31	10	0	G. J. Morgan, Esq. Mr. and Mrs. F. Platten. Edgar H. Padmore, Esq. Misses E. and L. Russell. Messrs. Wakeman Collins & Britton.
31	0	0	St. John Ambulance Brigade, Birmingham Nursing Corps.
30	15	0	Miss Elizabeth Prudames.

£	s.	d.	
30	7	0	The Municipal Players.
30	5	0	B. Goodman, Esq.
30	0	0	Mr. and Mrs. F. W. Greenway. Miss Julia Lloyd. J. F. Ratcliff (Metals) Ltd. Sir John Robertson.
28	18	9	Alfred Roberts & Sons Ltd.
28	13	1	Rudge-Whitworth Social Club (Wheels Branch).
28	8	9	Dr. Mary B. Stone.
28	3	6	King Edward's Grammar School for Girls, Camp Hill.
27	2	0	E. W. Bohle, Esq.
26	5	0	Aston Wilde & Co. Mr. and Mrs. Percy G. Allday. Bourne, Earle & Co. Ltd. Bakelite Ltd. Birmingham Printers Ltd. Professor J. C. Brash. Cuxon, Gerrard & Co. Cats Bros. Ltd. Duncan Flockart & Co. Professor I. de Burgh Daly. Dares Brewery Ltd. Mr. and Mrs. P. Everard. H. Incledon & Co. Ltd. T. Ireland, Esq. Jones & Foster Ltd. Lee, Longland & Co. Ltd. Mr. F. W. Mason Lamb. Henry T. Ledsam, Esq. Dr. W. J. McCardie. Baron A. Profumo. Alfred Preedy & Sons Ltd. R. Hugh Roberts, Esq. Richardson & Sons Ltd. Shakespeare & Vernon. Alfred Smith & Son. Singleton & Cole Ltd. A. C. Turner, Esq. Mr. and Mrs. Sydney Vernon. Dr. Thomas Wilson.
25	10	7	Balsall Peoples' Hospital Fund.
25	5	0	J. Norman Notchkiss, Esq.
25	0	0	J. and A. Albry. Miss E. S. Adkins. W. H. Abbott. Mr. and Mrs. L. W. Allen. A. Alexander, Esq. William Bailey (Birmingham) Ltd. A. Butcher, Esq. Alfred Brown & Co. British Thomson-Houston & Co. Ltd. E. C. Bewlay, Esq. Brightside Foundry & Engineering Co. Ltd. R. Ashby Bolton, Esq. Samuel Boddington, Esq. A. E. Booker Ltd. Councillor Harrison Barrow. Cincinnati Milling Machines Ltd. T. R. Canning, Esq. Cellon Ltd. Cooke & Murray. Frank Carver, Esq. Sir William Chance. C. H. Clarke, Esq. G. J. Dobbs, Esq. D. G. Denley, Esq. William Deakin & Co. Ltd. Edwin Danks & Co. Diespeker & Co. Ltd. Professor F. De Selincourt. Elkington & Co. Charles Ekin, Esq. Forrester Ketley & Co. J. H. Fulford, Esq. Holland W. Hobbis, Esq. John James, Esq., J.P. Mrs. F. Jolly. Miss J. Lloyd. Miss J. M. G. Lloyd. C. J. Lewis, Esq. Midland Counties Grocers' Protection & Benevolent Association. B. Mason & Sons Ltd. F. Marson, Esq. Mrs. H. C. Matthews. Councillor Miss Clara Martineau, J.P. Mr. and Mrs. George W. Mullins. National Boiler & General Insurance Co. Ltd. Stanley H. Parkes, Esq. Ephraim Phillips Ltd. Mrs. Sydney J. Ponten. A. E. Ralph & Co. Ltd. Dr. A. H. Railing. Philip H. Ryley. Lieut.-Colonel Anthony Rose. Smith & Davis Ltd. Harry Smith, Esq. Stewarts & Lloyds Ltd. William Sapcote & Sons. Sandoik British Agency Ltd. Mr. and Mrs. L. Arthur Smith. Stanley Bros. Ltd. Mr. and Mrs. P. M. Sturge. Sir Harry and Lady Spencer. Mr. and Mrs. Priestley Smith. Steel Band Conveyor & Engineering Co. Samuel Thornley Ltd. Tate & Lyle Ltd. United Wire Works (Birmingham) Ltd. Victor X-Ray Corporation Ltd. William Ward, Esq. Colonel C. J. H. Wheatley. G. Whitehouse, Esq. Wilson Lovatt & Sons Ltd.
24	12	1	Employees of Firmin & Sons Ltd.
24	0	0	Mrs. C. Sanger.
23	15	2	Balsall Working Men's Club & Institute.

£	s.	d.	
23	0	0	Andrew Alexander, Esq.
21	13	0	National Federation of Off-Licence Holders' Assocation.
21	0	0	Aga Heat Ltd. Anonymous. Anonymous. Mrs. A. Allison. Aerial Works Ltd. Birmingham County F.C. Birmingham Corporation Tramways & Omnibus Department. Chloride Electrical Storage Co. Ltd. Sir Austen Chamberlain, P.F., K.G., M.P. Estate of the late Henry Dowler. A. Edmonds & Co. Ltd. Rev. Charles H. Heath. George Heath Ltd. Sidney Hirst, Esq. Jaconello Ltd. Jarvis Bros. Councillor John W. Kerr. T. L. Lloyd, Esq. William L. Marian Ltd. Mrs. Adolf Myers. Michael Pearman, Esq. Councillor and Mrs. Harry Richardson. Llewellyn Ryland, Esq. Rookery Road Council School (Senior Dept). Siemens Electric Lamps & Supplies Ltd. J. T. Tittley, Esq. Silk & Frazier. W. H. Smart & Co. Ltd. Warriner & Mason Ltd.
20	10	0	City of Birmingham & District Butcher Sick & Dividend Society.
20	0	0	Aston Chain & Hook Co. Ltd. Anonymous. "In Memory of A.F." Staff of the Birmingham Chamber of Commerce. The Misses Baker. Miss Constance E. Brown. The Right Rev. Bishop A. Hamilton Baynes. Birmingham Caretakers' Association. Alan Cadbury, Esq. C. F. Crowder, Esq. Miss Mary Davies. Dr. H. Guy Dain. Sir John Ellerman, Bart. James Evans, Esq. Mr. and Mrs. David Gibbins. John Goode & Sons (Birmingham) Ltd. Trustees of George Fentham's Charity. Sir Walter and Lady Haworth. Frederick Jeavons & Co. Ltd. Lockerbie & Wilkinson Ltd. Mr. and Mrs. H. W. Lyde. Ernest R. Mason, Esq. Miss A. R. Southall. "Sam". Mr. and Mrs. G. Smart. G. W. Usher, Esq. Sidney Taunton, Esq. Wallis Williams, Esq. Mr. and Mrs. A. Winder.
19	19	0	Mulder M. Carter, Esq.
19	5	0	Bournville Friends' Meeting.
19	3	4	Birmingham Motoring Club Ltd.
19	3	0	For Miss D. M. Dunn.
17	16	9	Harry Vincent Ltd. (Visitors' Collecting Box).
17	12	0	Claude H. May, Esq.
17	4	0	Elliotts Metal Co. Ltd.
16	16	6	Members of Birmingham & District Master Plumbers' Association.
16	16	0	Miss Owen Rushton.
15	16	9	Selly Oak Friends' Meeting.
15	15	0	Acme Flooring & Paving Co. (1904) Ltd. Birmingham Funeral Directors' Guild. Birmingham Hebrew Congregation. James Cond Ltd. Cranes Screw & Colgryp Castor Co. Ltd. A. Frankenberg, Esq. C. W. Holcroft, Esq. B. W. T. Handley, Esq. Mr. and Mrs. J. E. Hempseed. Miss A. F. Marks. Charles A. Walker, Esq.
15	10	0	James Gibbons Ltd. Charles A. Walker, Esq.
15	5	0	Mr. and Mrs. T. D. F. Evans. Joseph Tomey & Son Ltd.
15	3	0	Vincents Social & Athletic Club.
15	0	0	Cox Oven Builders Ltd. W. Duckitt, Esq. Formin & Sons Ltd. The Right Hon. Lord Ilkeston. Reginald P. Lane, Esq. Mr. and Mrs. O. H. Stone. Employees of Showells Brewery Co. Ltd.
14	14	0	R. Platnauer Ltd.
14	7	0	J. E. Rubery, Esq.
13	13	0	Messrs. B. Holroyd, Esq. Anonymous.

128

£	s.	d.	
13	7	6	Bournville Dramatic Society.
13	5	0	Edgbaston Gun Club.
12	12	0	Thomas P. Hawkins & Son Ltd. Mr. and Mrs. A. E. Newton.
12	8	6	Girl Guides, King's Norton Division.
12	6	8	Publicity Club of Birmingham.
11	11	0	John Bailey, Esq. A. Steel, Esq.
11	0	0	Ed. J. Organ, Esq.
11	0	0	J. D. Maynard, Esq. Staff of Royal London Mutual Insurance Society (Small Heath Branch).
10	17	0	Staff of Liverpool & London & Globe Insurance Co. Ltd.
10	10	0	Aston Cabinet Co. Ltd. F. W. Aston, Esq. J. N. Atthill, Esq. Anonymous.

10 10 0 (continued) Aston Cabinet Co. Ltd. F. W. Aston, Esq. J. N. Atthill, Esq. Anonymous. C. Philip Achurch, Esq., M.B.E. S. J. Allen, Esq. J. C. Abbott & Co. Ltd. Anglo-American Oil Co. Ltd. Allcock & Co. Attlee, Edge & Lambert. Anonymous. Percy A. Abrahams, Esq. Bycroft & Co. Ltd. Blackheath Stamping Co. Ltd. Miss F. Catnach. George Baker Ltd. Brooks & Adams Ltd. J. Bailey, Esq. Dr. R. Tullis Baillie. Birmingham Wholesale Fruit & Potato Merchants' Association. William E. Benton, Esq. Brades' Welfare Society (William Hunt & Sons). H. B. Bradshaw Ltd. Mr. and Mrs. Eugene Baedeker. D. C. Brown, Esq. Birmingham Insurance Institute. Mr. and Mrs. A. E. N. Bulpitt. Councillor Miss H. Bartleet, O.B.E. Geo. Beech, Esq. Fred. Bochin, Esq. Dr. and Mrs. Guy Branson. Connolly & Olivieri Ltd. Collins Sedgwick & Co. Ltd. Mrs. Annie Combridge. Crawley, Parsons & Co. Ltd. Henry Cox Screw Co. Chambers & Remington. R. Cruickshank (Cellulose) Ltd. Alexander Comley Ltd. Car Mart Ltd. Frederick Carroll, Esq. Coventry Radiator & Presswork Co. Ltd. J. Smedley Crooke, Esq. T. N. Ducke & Sons. England & Sons Ltd. C. D. Eaton Ltd. Eaton & Wrighton. Agnes Edwards (Costumiers) Ltd. Employees of T. W. Edwards & Sons. Leonard Emmanuel, Esq. Fleetwood Deakin Hendricks & Co. Mr. and Mrs. William Fowler. Mrs. Helen Freeman. G. S. Ferguson, Esq. Mrs. H. Freeth. Gittings & Hill Ltd. The Grand Hotel. Gent & Co. Ltd. Goodbrand & Co. Ltd. Mrs. Greenway. Mrs. E. Greenway. Charles Gardner, Esq. Glazebrooks Ltd. T. Gibson, Esq. Mr. and Mrs. G. F. Goodman. W. H. Hart & Sons Ltd. Hunt & Milton Ltd. Harold Parker, Esq. Mrs. Amy A. Hawkins. Hussey, Egan & Pickmere Ltd. Harbuns Ltd. Charles H. Heath, Esq. Hudson, Scott & Sons Ltd. Innes, Smith & Co. Ltd. S. H. Johnson, Esq. Jenner & Co. Ltd. Kingfisher Ltd. Mrs. F. L. Kannreuther. Limmer & Trinidad Lake Asphalte Co. Ltd. C. H. Leng & Sons. F. H. Lloyd & Co. Ltd. J. Murray Laing, Esq. Lightfoot Refrigeration Co. Ltd. J. F. Luckman, Esq. Mr. and Mrs. A. H. Leaney. E. Anthony Lees, Esq., O.B.E. S. J. Moreland & Sons Ltd. Merry & Minton Ltd. J. & W. Mitchell Ltd. Lewis O. Mathews, Esq. Mrs. Edith M. Mathews. Metal Thread Screw Manufacturers' Association. W. G. Macnamara Ltd. Morris & Jacombs & Sons Ltd. S. C. Mendelsohn, Esq. Mining Research Laboratory. J. Matthews & Son. Francis J. Matthews. Miss Amy F. Marks. George H. Morley, Esq. Mr. and Mrs. T. E. Mitton. E. H. Newton, Esq. North British Rubber Co. Ltd. Northfield Children's Theatre. Sir Arthur Newsholme, M.D. Albert Phillips Ltd. C. P. Perry & Son Ltd. Power Petroleum Co. Ltd. Dr. H. H. Pollard. Postans Morley Bros. & Birtles Ltd. W. H. Robins, Esq. Miss Rosa F. Robins. Rollason, Abel & Sons Ltd.

£	s.	d.	
10	10	0	A. J. Rayment, Esq. Sir Charles Rafter, K.B.E. Dr. and Mrs. J. R. Ratcliffe. Rushton & Wilson. Rubery, Owen & Co. Ltd. Mrs. T. H. Russell. J. A. Reynolds & Co. Ltd. Smith & Ansell Ltd. Sun Cycles & Fittings Co. Ltd. W. H. Stoddard, Esq. James Siward, Esq. W. H. Smith & Son, & Holme. Shell-Mex & B.P. Ltd. J. Leonard Spicer, Esq. Smethwick Medical Society. G. A. Strasser, Esq. Mr. and Mrs. Charles Sangster. Shropshire Worcestershire & Staffordshire Electric Power Co. W. S. Shuttleworth & Co. Ltd. T. W. Simkin, Esq. Sanders & Mackenzie Ltd. A. D. Tipper, Esq. Miss Doris E. Tippetts, W. A. Taylor, Esq. Triplex Safety Glass Co. Ltd. Taylor, Law & Co. Ltd. Staff of H.M. Inspector of Taxes (1st District). W. J. Vincent, Esq. The Vono Co. Charles Wood, Esq. Wholesale Traders' Association. Wilson Carter & Pearson Ltd. Wood Carving Co. Ltd. Mrs. A. R. Young.
10	8	5	Employees of J. Gillott & Sons Ltd.
10	5	0	Frank W. Parsons, Esq.
10	0	0	Anonymous. Miss M. E. Adams. Miss C. E. Adams. Anonymous. Mr. and Mrs. Alfred Aston. In Memoriam, "J.G.B." "A former visitor to Edgbaston". Charles M. Alexander Copyrights Trust. The Rt. Hon. L. C. M. S. Amery, M.P. Anonymous. Birmingham Wholesale Meat Salesmen's Association. J. B. Bruce Ltd. Alfred Beebee Ltd. Mrs. Louis E. Bullock. H. Burman, Esq. L. Brecknell, Esq. Miss M. M. A. Burrows. Carrs (Birmingham) Ltd. Mr. and Mrs. R. H. Coates. Mr. and Mrs. Frank Chapman. Major P. H. Carter. Mr. and Mrs. Hugh B. Carslake. W. Duckitt, Esq. J. T. Darlington Ltd. E. Darby, Esq. A. E. Evans, Esq. Fathers of the Oratory. Anna Goodrick Ltd. Gabriel & Co. Ltd. Miss Ada Gibbins. Miss Martha Gibbins. Alan Geale, Esq. Gordon & Munro Ltd. Griffith & Diggens Ltd. Ham, Baker & Co. Ltd. J. G. Hammond, Esq. Mrs. Bertha Hope. Sir William Jaffray, Bart. Miss M. V. Johnson. Walter Johnson, Esq. W. E. Kenrick, Esq. Geoffrey Lloyd, Esq., M.P. William Lees & Sons Ltd. E. H. Maddocks, Esq. Howard Marsh, Esq. Moulded Products Ltd. Geoffrey E. Moore. Staff of Midland Hotel. Edward D. Mason, Esq. Mrs. A. M. Mathews. M. Mole & Sons Ltd. National Brick Co. Josiah Oldbury, Esq. Mrs. E. K. M. Osler. Miss Frances Petit. Miss I. C. Parsons. Rainsford & Lynes Ltd. W. Stephens, Esq. C. L. Taylor, Esq. Charles F. Thrackray Ltd. Professor J. Oliver Thomson. Mrs. H. H. Taylor. Christopher B. Taylor, Esq. Miss Agnes A. Wade. Lieut.-Colonel E. S. P. Wolferstan. Whittaker Ellis Ltd. Walter Williams Ltd. General and Mrs. Westmacott.

Contributions in Kind

It is only possible to mention a few of the special contributions to the scheme. Our thanks are due particularly to the following:

Messrs. Cadbury Brothers, for the gift to the City of the Centre Site, containing about a hundred acres of land reserved for hospital and medical school buildings.

The City of Birmingham, for their gift of the private roads and tree-lined verges at a cost of over £20,000.

130

Mr. A. E. Hills, whose gift of £25,000 wholly defrayed the cost of the equipment and fittings of the X-ray department.

Miss Doris Tippetts, for the gift of the coat-of-arms reproduced on the cover of this book.

Dr. Stanley Barnes, for the fitting up and furnishing of the chapel and mortuary chapel.

Mrs. G. J. Morgan, for the gift of the American organ to the main chapel.

Mrs. George Pearson, for organising the collection of a fund of over £4,000 for bed equipment.

The small committee headed by Mr. J. M. Nicolson and Mr. Frank Barnes, who, with the help of a few friends, planted the shrubs and trees, including some 2,000 hollies, and defrayed the cost of this valuable work.

APPENDIX C

RECEIPTS AND PAYMENTS FROM THE INCEPTION OF THE SCHEME TO JUNE 1950

	£ s. d.	£ s. d.
CASH RECEIVED:		
Donations and Legacies . . .		1,158,458 16 4
Bank Interest, *less* paid . . .		20,313 16 10
Investment Interest		9,089 8 5
Profit from Sale of Investment . .		1,082 6 0
Other Sundry Receipts (Rents, etc.) .		1,023 13 9
TOTAL RECEIPTS, April, 1928, to June, 1950		1,189,968 1 4
PAYMENTS:		
Buildings, Site Layout, Plant and Equipment (including fees for Architects, Engineers, Quantity Surveyors and Clerk of Works)	1,029,057 4 11	
University for Medical School . .	118,000 0 0	
Competition Awards to Architects .	3,075 0 0	
Expenses re Laying of Foundation Stone	3,065 16 9	
Administration Expenses . . .	33,991 16 4	
		1,187,189 18 0
BALANCE IN HAND at June 30th, 1950 . .		£2,778 3 4

APPENDIX D

FIGURES

ARCHITECT's estimates in 1933, for the sections of the hospital actually constructed were as follows:

£

Centre Block	247,000
Operating Theatres	48,000
Nurses' Home	174,000
Dispensary	11,000
Power House	27,000
Laundry	26,000
Mortuary	4,000
Roads	13,000

Items excluded from the first instalment included the casualty and out-patients' blocks, the fourth ward block, the chapel, the medical annexe, the night nurses' home, the maids' home, the pay block, and the residences of house governor and steward. The total estimates for these buildings amounted to about £300,000.

The cost of the Medical School, including equipment, was roughly £242,000.

In the course of the building operations, there were excavated some 150,000 cubic yards of earth. There were used 37,000 cubic yards of concrete, and there were employed 500 men continuously for five years. Bricks used totalled 17 million. In the hospital were used 6,400 tons and in the Medical School 500 tons of constructional steel.

The buildings occupy approximately 30 acres. The average height above sea level of the site is 495 feet. The height of the main hospital buildings is 105 feet, and of the tower is 176 feet above ground. The latter holds tanks containing 120,000 gallons of water.

The hospital has its own water supply from a bore-hole which is 450 feet deep, and which delivers 25,000 gallons an hour. A supply from municipal sources is also installed.

The reception hall in the nurses' home has a sprung dance floor measuring 170 feet by 50 feet.

There are 5 miles of drains, 4,300 windows with 25,000 panes of glass, and 3,200 doors.

The power house has four Lancashire boilers, each 30 feet by 9 feet, with automatic fuelling.

In a cold snap in the winter of 1938 the boilers were giving 29,000 lbs. of steam per hour, panel heat loss being 10 degrees. After heating up the buildings, the loss was only 3 degrees.

The hospital contains 6,344,000 cubic feet, and the Medical School 2,071,000 cubic feet.

The main contract for the hospital was signed in September, 1933, and the building was all ready for occupation on December 31st, 1938.

The Medical School contract was signed in March, 1936, and the building was ready for occupation in the spring of 1938.

APPENDIX E

REPORT OF THE SPECIAL COMMITTEE ON LAY-OUT

THE Report is based on visits made by the members of the committee to various hospitals in London, Rome, Genoa, Naples, Lyons, Paris, Hamburg, Copenhagen, Leipzig, and Helsingborg (Sweden).

REPORT

The following are the chief points we should like to bring to the Committee's notice:

1. There is considerable activity everywhere with regard to Hospitals.
2. Hospital service on the Continent is conceived on a much larger and more complete scale than in England. There is no division of Authority in health service and general hospitals provide for all types of illness.
3. In every city we visited we found large hospitals being erected three to five miles away from the centre.
4. These large Institutions contain, or are intended to contain, from 1,000 to 3,000 beds.
5. When a hospital centre is built outside, the main out-patient department remains in the centre of the city.
6. All the hospitals make generous provision for research by large departments for pathology, bacteriology and bio-chemistry.
7. The maintenance of hospitals is invariably a responsibility of the State or the Municipality, or both, and in Germany and Denmark finance presents little difficulty.
8. The cost of maintaining hospitals in Germany and Denmark is met as follows:
    The State accepts responsibility for medical education and for research in University hospitals. Practically all employed people contribute to an insurance scheme recognised by the State and hospital charges are paid to the Municipalities who, after a deduction for working expenses, make grants to the Hospitals.
9. In most cases (with the exception of the American Hospital in Paris, which is really a Nursing Home) the Hospitals are built on the Pavilion System, the Pavilions being usually widely separated and therefore occupying a large area.
10. All Authorities agree that the system of Pavilions spread over a large area is costly to build and to heat and very expensive to administer.
11. In Copenhagen the Municipal Authorities have decided to abandon the Pavilion System, owing to its costly administration; they have decided for this reason not to complete a large Pavilion Hospital, but instead to extend an old existing Institution built on a more concentrated plan known as the Corridor System. This will be explained in detail below.
12. Most Hospitals provide for paying patients of all classes.
13. In no case was the Medical Staff on English lines, but the practice is to appoint a small number of Medical, Surgical and Special Directors. The Medical Staff often gives either whole-time or nearly whole-time service, and is paid.

135

14. In Italy and France there is no trained Nursing Staff (with the exception of a part of the Policlinico at Rome); In Germany some of the Nurses are trained and others are untrained; in Denmark the Nursing is comparable to the English system.

15. The housing of Nurses in Italy, France and Germany is therefore a simple matter, and only in Denmark does it call for the same outlay as in England.

16. In the planning of Hospitals much more space is allotted to the administrative part of a Ward (Kitchen, Linen Room, Sister's Office, Larder, Day Room, Lavatories, etc.) than in England.

17. Most of the buildings seen were of three storeys, but the Children's Hospital at Leipzig and the new extension at the Charite (Berlin) are of four storeys. (An experienced Hospital Engineer at Copenhagen gave as his opinion that four storeys is the most economical and convenient. This view is confirmed by Mr. Cleland, the South African Architect.)

18. Provision is made everywhere for treatment in the open air, but the method employed varies.

19. There is a large percentage of chronic patients and more medical beds than surgical. In no case was the work anything like so intensive as in the Birmingham Voluntary Hospitals.

20. We found most Wards badly overcrowded, because all citizens have a right to treatment and must be admitted if they need it. Instead of the waiting lists common in England we found overcrowded wards.

21. Male labour is employed to a large extent instead of Ward Maids common in England.

22. With one exception there is an elaborate supply of lifts, always automatic.

23. A large number of observation beds is usually provided and all patients pass through them.

24. There is a tendency to divide the beds in a Ward Block into small groups.

25. In many instances there is a Special Diet Kitchen in addition to the General Kitchen.

GENERAL LAYOUT

We have plans and, in most cases, a description of all buildings seen by us.

The pavilions are nearly always widely separated. This arrangement originally arose from a desire to avoid infection, but it is now realised that the spread of infection can be prevented by simpler methods.

This separation necessitates the provision of covered communication ways and we found this problem tackled by different methods:

(a) By underground corridors having in several cases a railway for manual or electric traction.

(b) By twin corridors, one for service and one for staff and visitors.

(c) By a continuous covered corridor on the ground floor running completely round the Hospital and joined to one end of the Pavilions.

(d) By covered corridors on each floor.

(e) By placing a roof over the pathway connecting the Pavilions.

Sometimes communication is by open roads only, trolleys and wagons being propelled by hand or motor or drawn by ponies.

There is always a large administrative Block at the entrance containing, as a rule:

1. Casualty Rooms.

2. Out-patient Department.

3. Observation Beds.

4. Offices.

5. Resident Medical Officers' Quarters.

At Lyons, Out-patients will be seen in the city and also at the new Centre; but, at the latter, provision is made for Out-patients in several of the In-patient Blocks.

Operating Theatres are provided in different ways:

1. A pavilion containing only Operating Theatres.

2. A pavilion containing Operating Theatres and beds for patients awaiting operation and recovering from operation.

136

3.   Operating Theatre attached to Surgical pavilions.

The Research Departments are usually at the extreme end of the site behind the Ward Blocks. Spaces between the Pavilions are laid out as gardens.

WARD BLOCKS

The Wards tend to be divided into small units of twelve, six, four and two beds. The largest Ward seen contained twenty beds.

The space given to accessory rooms is often equal to the space available for beds.

It is a common practice to place lavatory basins in the Wards.

The beds are in some cases placed parallel to the side walls, so that the patients do not face a window but lie sideways to the light.

Everywhere provision is made for open air treatment, but the method varies:

(a)   By covered verandahs along the side of a Ward.

(b)   By balconies at the end of a Ward.

(c)   By balconies at the corner of a Ward when the long axis of the building faces south.

(d)   By sheds away from the Pavilions.

(e)   By shelters on the roof.

(f)   By solaria or covered-in balconies facing south.

The sanitary arrangements are very good and, by the use of marble or terrazzo floors and tiled walls, can be easily washed down.

In some instances Ward Annexes (Kitchens, Lavatories, etc.) are placed on the north side of a corridor and on the south side of the same corridor there are small Wards containing six, four, or two beds.

It is a common practice to provide a special room away from the Ward where patients are taken for dressing in a surgical pavilion and for examination in a medical pavilion.

In most cases the Ward floors are terrazzo and are drained so that they can be washed down. In some cases they are laid with linoleum; in others with magnesite composition and, in one case, with compressed cork. The magnesite floor is not durable and the cork floor has been in use only three months.

Terrazzo floors appear always subject to cracks but we noticed an attempt to counteract this tendency by laying it in sections.

In one hospital fixed wooden screens about six feet high were placed between sets of four and three beds. Some of us considered this gave greater privacy to the patients, but it has the disadvantage of the patient hearing sounds without being able to see whence they come, and for this reason an experienced Matron in the same city considered this an undesirable arrangement.

Metal is largely used for Ward furniture, and it is almost invariably the practice to paint beds, lockers, chairs and other furniture in the same colour. The effect is very good.

Although tiles may be used for dados, walls are generally painted with enamel.

Private patients are treated in special blocks or in rooms set apart in the Ward Blocks.

SPECIAL DEPARTMENTS

These have their own buildings.

In Germany and Denmark the Massage, Electrical and Hydro-therapeutic Departments are very large and well equipped.

The X-Rays Department is placed in a separate building but, in some cases, we found auxiliary X-Rays rooms in Surgical Blocks and Operating Departments.

TRAINING OF MEDICAL STUDENTS

In Rome the first line of buildings is devoted to the Medical School and is under the charge of whole-time Professors. The Medical School selects from the observation beds such patients as are likely to be valuable for medical education and sends them to its own Wards. Consequently the other parts of the hospital are filled with cases that are not required for teaching purposes. The observation beds are under a different staff. Patients remain in them only twenty-four hours, and the system creates healthy rivalry in accurate and rapid diagnosis.

At the Eppendorf (Hamburg) there is no School in the ordinary sense, although students are received. A great deal of research is done here, but primarily as a part of treatment, and the University makes use of the very fine Scientific Block only by permission of the Hospital Authorities.

At the Barmbeck (Hamburg) there is complete provision for medical education under State control and the Professors and students have access to all departments.

At Copenhagen the Medical School is attached to the Rigshospital (*i.e.*, State Hospital), for which the State is mainly responsible. There is here a large, well-equipped Block, both on the Medical and Surgical side under the control of two Professors of Medicine and two Professors of Surgery. These contain laboratories, fine lecture theatres, record rooms, libraries and study rooms for students, and consulting rooms where the Professors see both hospital and private patients. The Professors give practically their whole time to the Hospital and are resident. In addition there are resident whole-time Professors of Gynaecology, Ophthalmology, etc.

At Berlin there is a very well-equipped Medical School attached to the Charite.

THE CORRIDOR SYSTEM

In order to understand this type of building it will probably be necessary to examine the plans which were given to us of the Copenhagen Kommune and County Hospitals.

A corridor runs the whole length of the Ward Block. The Kitchen, Bathroom, Lavatories, Linen Rooms, Larder, etc., are placed on the north side of this corridor. On the south side there is a succession of small rooms for patients containing six, four or two beds.

———

Everywhere, without exception, the deputation was most kindly received. Everyone was anxious to do all they could to help and ready to put themselves to inconvenience to shew their Hospitals and to explain methods.

Several times we learned of an important hospital hitherto unknown to us and paid a prolonged visit without notice beforehand, but that made no difference to the welcome offered. And it has to be remembered that the demands upon our hosts were sometimes exceptional owing to the difficulty of language.

The Official Representatives of our own country and of the several cities visited were just as considerate, and entertained us in a generous manner. We are glad to know that the Lord Mayor has sent thanks to those to whom we feel so much indebted.

Signed,

G. J. EMANUEL.
A. H. LEANEY.
J. B. LEATHER.
H. H. SAMPSON.

May 7th, 1927.

138

APPENDIX F

METCHLEY PARK ESTATE

SUMMARY OF RESTRICTIONS, ETC., CONTAINED IN THE CONTRACT FOR SALE (ABRIDGED)

1. The premises shall not be used except for the following purposes:
   (a) Agricultural pastural or horticultural purposes.
   (b) For purposes of or in connection with a hospital or hospitals, but subject to the restrictions thereinafter contained.
   (c) Schools for medical students or nurses or members of ambulance first aid or similar societies or bodies.
   (d) Hostels for medical students or nurses.
   (e) Pleasure grounds for use by hospitals or scholastic institutions.
2. No buildings shall be erected except as above.
3. No hospital or other building erected on the said premises shall be used for the general treatment of:
   (a) Insanity or lunacy.
   (b) The following infectious diseases: Cholera, small-pox, typhus, plague, scarlet fever, measles.
4. No laundry or power house to be built north of a line indicated on the attached map.
5. Maintain fences and plant trees in specified areas.

NOTE ON THE LEASE FROM THE CORPORATION TO THE BIRMINGHAM HOSPITALS CENTRE
(Abridged)

(a) First lease of 22.105 acres, adjacent to the area proposed to be leased to the University for the Medical School. Lease is for 999 years at a rent of £22 : 2 : 0 a year. The Centre to pay in addition £230 a year towards paying for road maintenance. The University to pay £35 per annum for the same purpose.
(b) Not to allow the premises to be used for football matches, firework displays, etc., for which a charge is made for admission, nor for the display for profit of advertisements.
(c) Provisions for the safeguarding of the Elan Valley Aqueduct.

INDEX

143